# THE OFFICIAL
# MANCHESTER
# UNITED
# CROSSWORD BOOK

First edition published in 2004

Manufactured and distributed by
Manchester United Books
an imprint of Carlton Books Limited
20 Mortimer Street, London W1T 3JW

A CIP catalogue record for this book is available from the British Library

ISBN 0 233 00101 8

Project editor: Martin Corteel
Editorial assistant: David Ballheimer
Design: Darren Jordan
Production: Lisa French

Printed in Great Britain

# THE OFFICIAL
# MANCHESTER UNITED
# CROSSWORD BOOK

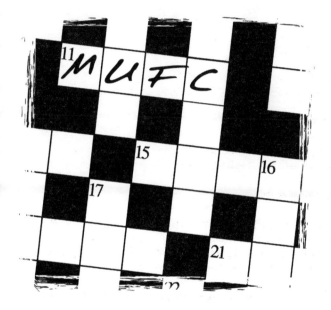

## 50 CROSSWORD PUZZLES
## TOTALLY DEVOTED TO UNITED

### COMPILED BY THOMAS TRICKETT

# Introduction

Welcome to the *Official Manchester United Crossword Book*.

Here you will find a collection of 50 crossword puzzles which will tax the minds of the most ardent United fans. The clues have been designed to test, and even expand, your knowledge of your favourite football club. We have sought to appeal to every generation of puzzler by providing clues that give answers that range back to the earliest days of Newton Heath right up to the present day, delving into Manchester United's illustrious history.

The clues range from the reasonably straightforward – requiring the names of individual players – to more specialist ones, asking for players' nicknames or future or past clubs. There are playful posers in which the answer is hidden in the clue and anagrams which require unscrambling. If you are determined to solve every clue of every puzzle, you will find it useful to have a couple of reference books at your side. Most of the answers can be found in either *The Official Manchester United Illustrated History* or *The Official Manchester United Illustrated Encyclopedia*, both published by Carlton Books.

The puzzles come from the rich heritage which makes Manchester United the remarkable club it is or from the wider world of football. All facts and figures are as of the end of the 2003–04 FA Barclaycard Premiership season.

Thomas Trickett

# Acknowledgements

We would like to express our thanks to Mr Keith Davis for his invaluable technical skill in the creation of this book. Other acknowledgements go to our Sport Consultant, Mr Arthur Llewellyn, whose incredibly wide knowledge of sports has helped this project go according to plan. Assistant researchers Nathalie Antonia Llewellyn, Louise Gould and Nuala Alys also deserve recognition for the alacrity with which they dealt with the occasional obstacles that arose.

# The Crosswords

## Across

**1** Home ground of club that winger Mickey Thomas left to join United in 1978 (10)

**8** Nationality of 1960s/70s United midfielder, Carlo Sartori (7)

**9** - - - - - Forlan, Montevideo born 2000s United striker (5)

**10** It's tossed to choose ends (4)

**11** Hugh - - - -, United forward 1903–04 not 2000s Republic of Ireland coach Brian though! (4)

**12** Argue with tier at Old Trafford stadium, maybe! (3)

**14** Queens Park Rangers side upsets United team, apparently (6)

**15** Report 1938–44 United manager, Jimmy (anag) (6)

**18** United apprentice is only too glad to be a youngster, apparently (3)

**20** - - - - Webb, 1980s/90s United midfielder (4)

**21** In 1990s United changed shirts at half-time at this ground (4)

**23** For penalties a ball is placed - - - - - spot (2, 3)

**24** Mike - - - - - - -, Southampton striker played against United in 1976 FA Cup final (7)

**25** Ex-United keeper Harry Gregg managed this Town club 1968–72 (10)

## Down

**1** Birthplace of *20 across* (7)

**2** Kick ball in a high arc type of way (4)

**3** Star sign of ex-United defender, Gordon McQueen (6)

**4** Not the favourite type of team to visit Old Trafford (8)

**5** Type of abusive words not accepted by some referees (5)

**6** - - - Bobby - - - - - - - -, knighted United 1950s/60s/70s forward (3, 8)

**7** What the 5 was in the old 2-3-5 formation, such as Best, Law, Charlton, Herd and Connelly (7, 4)

**13** 1970s/80 international winger Steve Coppell was signed from this club 1975 (8)

**16** Paul - - - - - - -, 2000s United squad midfielder (7)

**17** Bits of set plays (6)

**19** Nationality of 1990s/2000s United defender Jaap Stam (5)

**22** Colloquial term for the Red Devils (3, 1)

## Across

**1** Electric cup upset (5)
**4** – – – – – of the Titans, like United v Arsenal (5)
**10** French club, opponents of United in 2001 Champions League (5)
**11** Nobby Stiles was sent-off against FK – – – – – – – Vienna in 1966 (7)
**12** Result Feyenoord – – –, United – – – – –, Champions League match 1997 (3, 5)
**13** Old Trafford is not United's away ground (4)
**15** United were not the winners 1976 FA Cup final! (6)
**17** Term for dull and uninteresting game (6)
**19** Unfavoured colour for 1990s United away kit (4)
**20** Month in which 1990s/2000s Reds midfielder Paul Scholes was born (8)
**23** Football ground subways, perhaps (7)
**24** Amount of times United won FA Cup in the 1980s (5)
**25** Nickname of club from whom United signed Tommy Taylor in 1953 (5)
**26** Roger – – – – –, 1950s United captain (5)

## Down

**2** Aaron – – – – –, 1900s United full-back (5)
**3** Popular county where many United players reside (8)
**5** Fixture – – – – (4)
**6** Carlo – – – – – – –, United midfielder 1968/7? (7)
**7** They were officially switched on at Old Trafford in 1957 (11)
**8** Penalties can be missed, scored or – – – – – (5)
**9** Jay revs game to show Newton Heath goalkeeper (anag) (5, 6)
**14** Ex-United midfielder Gordon Strachan managed this club, 1996–2001 (8)
**16** Alex – – – – – – –, United goalkeeper 1966–78 (7)
**18** Full dwelling for capacity crowd at Old Trafford (5)
**21** – – – – – McClair, 1980s/90s United forward (5)
**22** United legend Billy Meredith hides lake, apparently (4)

## Across

1 Tommy – – – – – – –, 1970s United forward (7)
7 – – – – – Leverkusen ended United's Champions League dreams in 2002 (5)
8 – – – – – – – Pearson, 1930s/40s/50s United & England international (7)
9 United relies on this Belgian League side to appear (anag) (6)
11 Club defeated by United in 1999 Champions League quarter-final (5)
13 United won the 2003 Premier– – – – (4)
14 – – – – – – – Blanc, 2000s United defender (7)
15 Participate in game (4)
16 Trophy United first won in 1909 (1,1, 3)
17 Noisy old fashioned football fan accessory (6)
21 – – – – – – – Iddon, 1920s United forward, but not singer Cliff! (7)
22 Colour of Old Trafford pitch surface, perhaps! (5)
23 Type of test for injury recovering player (7)

## Down

2 Ex-United boss Ron Atkinson managed this club 1991–94 (5, 5)
3 Only lend 1900s/10s United full-back, Tony (anag) (8)
4 New thought for ideal strategy, apparently (4)
5 Bar Irwin from playing for this Italian side, apparently (4)
6 Defender Johnny Carey was 1949 Football of the – – – – (4)
9 Not an earlier kick-off (5)
10 Leg protectors not pads though! (4, 6)
12 Dive in, fencing style, for a tackle (5)
13 Gordon – – – – – – – –, 1980s United & Scotland international (8)
18 Ex-United forward Willie Morgan left Old Trafford for – – – – Moor (4)
19 1990s/2000s Ryan Giggs' national vegetable also found in Staffordshire town (4)
20 Type of small car for five-a-side football, maybe! (4)

## Across

**1** The referee has used the whistle (5)
**7** Rearrange phone jar for Newton Heath forward (anag) (4, 4)
**8** Teams or sides (5)
**10** Matt Busby signed this 1940s/50s United defender (4, 6)
**12** Age of David Beckham when he made his full United debut (8)
**14** Is Les Sealey surrounded by water, apparently (4)
**16** Doorbell hides 1900s/1910s United half-back Alex, apparently (4)
**17** James, 1900s Newton Heath/United goalkeeper, was about under SAS (anag) (8)
**20** Pitch test (10)
**23** Bobby – – – – –, United defender 1965/67 (5)
**24** Players wages (8)
**25** Roy Keane made his United – – – – – against Norwich City 1993 (5)

## Down

**1** Martin – – – – – –, 1970s/80s United captain (6)
**2** Neil – – – –, 1980s/90s United & England midfielder (4)
**3** Illegal challenge (4)
**4** FA Cup is a – – – – –out competition (5)
**5** Gary – – – – – – – – –, ex-United defender 1989/98 (9)
**6** Joe – – – – – –, played over 500 United games (6)
**9** Position United finished 1990–91 season (5)
**11** Fence feature of football stadium (9)
**13** Period of time to see Ray Wilkins play at Old Trafford, apparently (3)
**15** PFA for instance (5)
**16** Gary – – – – – –, 1970s/80s United goalkeeper (6)
**18** Previous home before Old Trafford was Bank – – – – – – (6)
**19** Red United player (nick) (5)
**21** Marks a player with labels (4)
**22** Type of book carried by referee (4)

## Across

6 Calm chile egg reveals 1990s/2000s United defender (anag) (7, 5)
8 Ex-United boss Tommy Docherty managed Queens Park - - - - - - - 1978–79 (7)
9 Ex-United star Dennis Viollet managed this club 1971 (5)
10 Part of the foot used for back pass, perhaps! (4)
12 Unsuccessful football result (6)
14 Rescued a penalty (5)
15 Ruud Van Nistelrooy won the 2003 - - - - - - Boot Award (6)
16 Charlton, Law & Best form a riot (anag) (4)
19 Eventually the game takes place, apparently (5)
21 Ball is positioned on here for penalty kicks (3, 4)
22 Britain's most expensive defender when signed from Leeds in 2002 (3, 9)

## Down

1 Noon cell reveals ex-United half-back, Pat (anag) (1'7)
2 Mexican or tidal at Old Trafford, perhaps! (5)
3 Hot drink container, handy for winter matches (5)
4 Selected for team by using a voting system, apparently (7)
5 So greedy player conceals a giant monster, apparently (4)
6 1980s/90s United and Wales striker, later national coach (4, 6)
7 Most of 1990s/2000s United forward Ryan Giggs shots are - - - - - - - - - - (4-6)
11 - - - Ure, 1960s/70s United defender (3)
12 Water condensation rising on a football pitch (3)
13 United won the 1968 - - - - - - - - - Cup Final (8)
14 Kevin Moran became the first player to be - - - - - - - in an FA Cup Final (4, 3)
17 Shining football celebrities like Best, Beckham & Giggs (5)
18 - - - - - Irwin, 1990s/2000s United defender signed from Oldham Athletic (5)
20 Badness found in the Red Devils, apparently (4)

**Across**

**3** Trophy upsets (3, 6)
**8** – – – – Giggs, 1990s/2000s United midfielder/striker (4)
**9** Darren – – – – – – – –, Edinburgh born 2000s United midfielder (8)
**10** Lou, turned down Liverpool to sign for United 1973 (6)
**13** Fitness trials (5)
**14** Change course of ball (7)
**15** This pitch is black and might be found in the Old Trafford car park (3)
**16** Type of throwing option for ex-United keeper, Fabian Barthez (7)
**17** Domestic trophy United have won many times (1,1, 3)
**21** – – – – – – Burke, 1940s United forward (6)
**22** – – – – – – – – Hilditch, United manager 1926–27 (8)
**23** Individual runs, perhaps! (4)
**24** United's matchday competitors (9)

**Down**

**1** United gained this to Division One in 1975 (9)
**2** Joe, ancestral 1940s/50s United goalkeeper (anag) (9)
**4** Out of condition footballer (5)
**5** Charlie – – – – – – –, 1920s United & England international half-back (7)
**6** Amount of times United won *17 across* in the 1970s (4)
**7** Goalkeepers hide room in fortress, apparently (4)
**11** Noted corn for Liverpool-born 1900s/10s United forward (anag) (3, 9)
**12** Frank – – – – – – – – –, 1980s United and Republic of Ireland striker (9)
**14** Sir Alex was adamant, this was the way to block the leaky defence, apparently (3)
**15** Alter part of counter attack to thrash opposition (anag) (7)
**18** Manchester United is situated in – – – – – Britain (5)
**19** Applaud good football (4)
**20** Get Rio Ferdinand involved in a set of three, apparently (4)

## Across

 1  Teddy – – – – – – – – – –, 1990s/2000s United and England striker (10)
 8  First games of the season, perhaps! (7)
 9  Alter angel for corner of woodwork frame (anag) (5)
10  Change mate for United side (anag) (4)
11  George Best was a 1960s football – – – – not pop though! (4)
12  If the Royal Air Force is intially found in Old Trafford, this rodent is found in Fratton Park, apparently (3)
14  – – – – – – Albiston made his United debut in 1974 League Cup (6)
15  Score draw involving two goals (3, 3) (6)
18  Place for match fans to drink alcohol (short) (3)
20  Amount of times United won the European Cup in the 1960s (4)
21  Jaap – – – –, former United defender (4)
23  John –'– – – –, 1990s United full-back (1'4)
24  Nationality of 1990s United opponents Torpedo Moscow (7)
25  A bin bridge will reveal 1946 forward, Bill, who scored on his only Reds appearance (anag) (10)

## Down

 1  Alter swatter for Mr Houston, the 1970s/80s defender (anag) (7)
 2  Eleven players inaccurately comprise this, apparently (4)
 3  United legend Denis Law was not a centre-forward (6)
 4  Ball must cross over this fully to become a score (4-4)
 5  Annoy Alex Ferguson when he played for Rangers FC, apparently (5)
 6  Conquerors of Manchester United in the 1976 FA Cup Final (11)
 7  Country Manchester United visited when beating Borussia Dortmund in 1964 (4, 7)
13  – – – – – – – – Cup, precursor of the Champions League, won by United in 1968 (8)
16  Opposite position to *3 down* for ex-United forward, John Aston (7)
17  Ruud Van Nistelrooy was the English Premiership's top goal – – – – – – in 2003 (6)
19  Brag about this Sporting Portuguese League side, apparently (5)
22  Employed the ball (4)

## Across

**1** Knocked out Manchester United from 2003–04 Champions League (5)

**4** – – – – – Bruce, 1980s/90s United captain (5)

**10** CSKA – – – – –, capital Bulgarian League side (5)

**11** Dismiss with red card (4, 3)

**12** United – – – – – – – – RSC Anderlecht 10–0 in 1956 (8)

**13** Alter sale for ex-United defender Laurent Blanc's birthplace (anag) (4)

**15** – – – – – – one shirt for 1990s United keeper, Mr Schmeichel (6)

**17** Ex-United midfielder Lee Sharpe was left– – – – – – (6)

**19** Shirt number for ex-United legend, Bobby Charlton (4)

**20** Position for ex-United player, Denis Irwin (8)

**23** Matt – – – – – – –, 1990s/2000s Leicester City defender played against United in 2003 Worthington Cup tie (7)

**24** Alter part of football trial to find the scent (anag) (5)

**25** 1920s United forward David was really nervous, apparently (5)

**26** George – – – – –, ex-United forward sounds like Millwalls nickname (5)

## Down

**2** Bid for a player who put off errant move, apparently (5)

**3** Player switch from club to club (8)

**5** – – – – Dunne, 1960s/70s United full-back (4)

**6** Dennis – – – – – – –, 1950s/60s United & England forward (7)

**7** – – – – – – – – – –Lyne, Manchester district where 1990s United forward Mark Robins was born (6-5)

**8** Express ex-United player into English county, apparently (5)

**9** What some people call football's most misunderstood law (7, 4)

**14** United players do not speak when sent to this club (8)

**16** Thomas – – – – – – –, 1940s/50s United full-back (7)

**18** United season ticket-holders have booked their own (5)

**21** Sketched a goalless game! (5)

**22** Andy – – – –, United striker joined Blackburn Rovers in 2002 (4)

## Across

1 Country of birth of 1990s/2000s midfielder, Roy Keane (7)
7 Team which ended United's reign as European Cup holders, 1969 (5)
8 Clumsy goalkeeping mistake! (7)
9 United's opponents in 1996 FA Cup semi-final (6)
11 Manchester United conceals part of the body, apparently (5)
13 Successful records when ball touches bar (4)
14 Country where United played Sturm Graz in 1999 Champions League (7)
15 – – – – Davies, tragic 1980s United forward (4)
16 Flocks of Norwich, Swansea, Crystal Palace, Swindon and Brighton nicknames (5)
17 Safe term for 2000s United's Tim Howard (6)
21 Quinton – – – – – – –, 1990s/2000s United & South African international (7)
22 – – – – – Lewis, 1950s United forward (5)
23 Goal opportunities (7)

## Down

2 1980s/90s United forward signed from Dundee United (5, 5)
3 Previous title of assistant referee (8)
4 – – – – Cantwell, 1960s United full-back (4)
5 Gordon – – – –, 1970s United winger (4)
6 An early one, colloquially, for a red-carded player! (4)
9 United v Blackburn Rovers match hides cricket term, apparently (5)
10 Match crowd count (10)
12 Acting award for 1900s/10s United full-back, – – – – – Linkson (5)
13 1932–37 United boss Scott Duncan also managed this Scottish side (8)
18 Stretford amongst others! (4)
19 – – – – Nevland, 1990s/2000s United & Norway forward (4)
20 Ex-United superstar, David Beckham married – – – – Spice! (4)

## Across

1 Nationality of 2000s United striker, Ruud Van Nistelrooy (5)
7 David Beckham left Old Trafford for El Stadio - - - - - - - - Bernabeu (8)
8 Ex-United striker Dion Dublin joined this side 1998 (5)
10 United winger played in 1983 FA Cup final (4, 6)
12 Real - - - - - - - -, Spanish club but not the team Beckham joined (8)
14 1930s United forward not 1990s/2000s England striker Michael though! (4)
16 Alex - - - -ney, was Reds goalkeeper when the four- - - - - law came in (4)
17 Birth month of 1990s United keeper, Peter Schmeichel (8)
20 1980s, United & Scotland international forward (4, 6)
23 Magnificent 1960s United full-back, Bobby (5)
24 Forename of 1926/27 United manager, Mr Hilditch (8)
25 Alter posts when play ceases (anag) (5)

## Down

1 Ron - - - - - -, 1970s United & Wales striker, unrelated to *10 across* (6)
2 United were runners-up in the Coca- - - - - Cup 1994 (4)
3 - - - - McCartney, author of Duncan Edwards book *The Full Report* (4)
4 When Sir Alex's team plays badly, this comes out of his ears, apparently (5)
5 Chelsea player who made his debut against United in 1968 (5, 4)
6 Bryan - - - - - -, longest serving captain in United history (6)
9 Tall Englishman reveals 1950s United goalkeeper, apparently (5)
11 He-man clan reveals 1920s/30s United player, Hugh (anag) (9)
13 Ex-United striker Danny Wallace was a top player, apparently (3)
15 - - - - - Pilkington, 1990s United goalkeeper (5)
16 Suddenly seize a victory, maybe! (6)
18 Martyn - - - - - -, 1970s United defender (6)
19 Dion Dublin came to Old Trafford from the - - - - - Stadium, 1992 (5)
21 1900s United goalkeeper Archie Montgomery hid architectural feature, apparently (4)
22 United - - - - to Liverpool 2–0 Worthington Cup Final 2003 (4)

## Across

**6** 1970s/80s, United winger arrived from Tranmere Rovers (5, 7)

**8** Ex-United skipper Bryan Robson gained 90 caps for this country (7)

**9** Paul Scholes made his United – – – – – – against Ipswich 1994 (5)

**10** *1 down* started his managerial career at – – – – Stirlingshire (4)

**12** Three trophies for United in 1999 (6)

**14** Days at the – – – – –, watching horses run is a hobby for many United players (5)

**15** *1 down* was a forest warden when playing for Rangers, apparently (6)

**16** – – – – van Nistelrooy, 2000s United striker (4)

**19** Ex-United keeper Harry Gregg managed this Cheshire side 1975–77 (5)

**21** Alter remands to find 1920s/30s United forward, Charlie (anag) (7)

**22** 1990s/2000s United and Wales winger Ryan Giggs was born in nineteen – – – – – – – – – – – – (7, 5)

## Down

**1** Alex – – – – – – – –, took charge as manager of United in 1986 (8)

**2** Reward for making cup final (5)

**3** Was John – – – – – a temperamental 1930s Reds goalkeeper? (5)

**4** Nickname of Scottish side *1 down* once played with, not Gers though! (7)

**5** Manchester United Football – – – – (4)

**6** 1980s/90s United defender who managed in the Premier League in 2003–04 (5, 5)

**7** Number of persons present at Old Trafford game (10)

**11** Spoil the game by marking ex-United striker Mark Hughes, apparently (3)

**12** – – – MacDougall, 1970s United striker (3)

**13** Park in Oldham for which Martin Buchan left Old Trafford in 1983 (8)

**14** Match official (7)

**17** Ex-United forward Lou Macari rates being angry, apparently (5)

**18** Common English surname for 1930s United forward, Jack (5)

**20** It seems you hide Veron for eternity, apparently (4)

## Across

**3** Romantic day for ex-United goalkeeper, Bob (9)

**8** Change ride for 1920s/30s United forward, Tom (anag) (4)

**9** Numerically speaking the last selected player (8)

**10** Prague club which sold Karel Poborsky to United (6)

**13** Traditional colour of United shorts (5)

**14** Kicked ball may sometimes swerve from course (7)

**15** Secreted each identity on the team sheet, apparently (3)

**16** Tell trainer to take refresher course (anag) (7)

**17** Did Ryan's brother Rhodri Giggs apparently grab a cup when he signed for this Borough club in 2003? (5)

**21** 1990s/2000s, United midfielder Paul Scholes is nicknamed the Ginger – – – – – – (6)

**22** Sanction a player for an indiscretion, especially in *4 down* (8)

**23** Alter loos for individual run (anag) (4)

**24** Norman, United striker 1981–89 (9)

## Down

**1** There's many a – – – – – – – – – from Sir Alex after a poor performance (5, 4)

**2** United and Millwall were 2004 FA Cup – – – – – – – – – (9)

**4** 18 x 44 yd penalty spaces found on football pitch (5)

**5** Hooligan is removed from ground (7)

**6** Bootlaces are drawn for cup game (4)

**7** Nest found in goalmouth (anag) (4)

**11** Toned corn reveals 1900s/10s United forward (anag) (3, 6)

**12** Frank – – – – – – – – – –, 1980s United & Rep of Ireland forward (9)

**14** The noise from the Carrington dining room, apparently (3)

**15** Mark – – – – – – –, 1980s United defender not snooker legend Hurricane though! (7)

**18** What the manager must to do improve the United squad (5)

**19** Goal netting (4)

**20** Teddy Sheringham left Old Trafford for White – – – – Lane, 2001 (4)

## Across

**1** United midfielder Paul Tierney went on-loan to this club 2004 (10)
**8** Nationality of 1990s/2000s, United midfielder Quinton Fortune (7)
**9** United beat – – – – – Warsaw, 1991 European Cup-winners Cup (5)
**10** 1970s United midfielder Gerry Daly on loan with French League side, apparently (4)
**11** – – – – Djemba-Djemba, 2000s Cameroon and United midfielder (4)
**12** – – – Wilkins, 1970s/80s United and England midfielder (3)
**14** Neck attachment to United shirt, perhaps! (6)
**15** Hang one's boots up (6)
**18** It's not on when red carded (3)
**20** A non-league side will play at Old Trafford soon, apparently (4)
**21** United beat Arsenal 1–0 FA Cup – – – – -final 2004 (4)
**23** – – – – – Bond, 1950s United forward (5)
**24** – – – – – – – Lane, Sheffield, where United lost 1993 FA Cup tie (7)
**25** Draft Wales makes 1920s/30s United goalkeeper (anag) (3, 7)

## Down

**1** Roy, 1990s/2000s United goalkeeper (7)
**2** Good fortune for 2000s United's Quinton, maybe! (4)
**3** Dry hen shows Newton Heath forward, James (anag) (6)
**4** Picked to play (8)
**5** Street where United beat Hereford 6–0 in 2001–02 friendly (5)
**6** Salford-born 1990s/2000s United midfielder/forward (4, 7)
**7** 1990s/2000s, United and England defender (4, 7)
**13** Ron Atkinson, Frank O'Farrell, etc. have been United's (8)
**16** Ex-United midfielder Lee Sharpe left for this cold country in 2003 (7)
**17** United achieved a domestic – – – – – – in 1993–94 season (6)
**19** Match which follows *21 across* (5)
**22** Louis – – – –, 2000s United striker bought from Fulham (4)

## Across

**1** 1930s United striker Billy Boyd also played for Scottish side nicknamed The Bully Wee (5)

**4** Clayton – – – – –more, 1980s/90s United utility player (5)

**10** Jesper – – – – –, 1980s United forward (5)

**11** Country for 1996 United opponents Rapid Vienna (7)

**12** David – – – – – – – –, ex-United forward not former athlete Linford though! (8)

**13** City hidden by ex-United forward Dwight Yorke, apparently (4)

**15** Birthplace of 1990s/2000s United defender David May (6)

**17** Manchester architects Atherden – – – – – – worked on the Old Trafford stadium (6)

**19** Transfer – – – –, where a want-away player goes (4)

**20** Merseyside club which signed 1950s United goalkeeper Gordon Clayton (8)

**23** Fluid pieces of interplay involving two players (3-4)

**24** Listen to a United match via this medium (5)

**25** 1941 a German bomb nearly demolished the Main – – – – – at Old Trafford (5)

**26** Not a lower terrace at Old Trafford (5)

## Down

**2** FA Cup final runner-up is not a winner (5)

**3** 1960s/70s United and Scotland forward (5, 3)

**5** The – – – – time Eric Cantona played for United was in 1997 (4)

**6** Roy – – – – – – –, United keeper joined from Wigan in 2001 (7)

**7** Moth control reveals 1910s United full-back who might have been at home in – – – – – – – – -cum-Hardy (anag) (3, 8)

**8** – – – – – May, United defender 1990s/2000s (5)

**9** Jean Bedrock shows 1930s/40s United goalkeeper (anag) (4, 7)

**14** Not a winning United player 1979 FA Cup final (6, 2)

**16** Offence which now gets a free-kick moved ten yards and brings a yellow card (7)

**18** Nationality of former United defender, Denis Irwin (5)

**21** – – – – – Colman, Busby Babe half-back (5)

**22** Regarding United defenders although a brother Gary Neville is not Phil's (4)

**Across**

**1** 1920s United full-back Charlie was in the Bradford team, apparently (7)

**7** Steve, 1960s/70s United half-back (5)

**8** "– – – – – – – the Belfast Boy", Mr Best (7)

**9** Player needs re-match (anag) (6)

**11** New thoughts are needed if on losing streak (5)

**13** 1980s United forward Jesper Olsen signed from this Amsterdam side (4)

**14** Dry patch for out of form striker (7)

**15** Requests for a transfer (4)

**16** Type of sheet countless Old Trafford goalkeepers have kept (5)

**17** 2000s United forward Ruud Van Nistelrooy is a master at staying – – – – – – when he makes a run (6)

**21** It's all about survival of the – – – – – – – in extra-time (7)

**22** – – – – – Wallace, 1980s/90s United striker (5)

**23** Putting the ball on penalty spot (7)

**Down**

**2** Sole and wax reveals 1950s/60s United forward (anag) (4, 6)

**3** Not defenders for Kanchelskis, Charlton and Law (8)

**4** Alter Iran for cause of wet football pitch (anag) (4)

**5** Alter ales for player auction, perhaps (anag) (4)

**6** David Beckham joined – – – – Madrid in 2003 (4)

**9** Rangers shot is out of scope for United's goal, apparently (5)

**10** Can mad oars make Newton Heath forward (anag) (4, 6)

**12** Alcohol George Best has tried to beat (5)

**13** Could this be Bobby Charlton's second side? (8)

**18** – – – – Brennan, 1950s/60/70s United and Republic of Ireland defender (4)

**19** Nickname of the first club where Sir Alex won a European cup (4)

**20** – – – – Foulkes, legendary 1950s/60s/70s United defender (4)

## Across

1 Not aways on football coupon (5)
7 Old Trafford for United & Prenton Park for – – – – – – – Rovers (8)
8 White pitch markings (5)
10 Honest pens reveals Newton Heath forward (anag) (10)
12 Goalkeeper Pat Dunne arrived from – – – – – – – – Rovers in 1964 (8)
14 Cross woodwork features (4)
16 Dutch opponents from the capital met United in 1976 UEFA Cup (4)
17 England defender sent off against United at Highbury in 2002–03 season (8)
20 Football crowds but not necessarily supporters though! (10)
23 Did Gordon Strachan have a halo when managing Southampton (nick) (5)
24 Joe Jordan represented this country while at United (8)
25 Eddie – – – – –, 1950s United forward (5)

## Down

1 It's a game of two (6)
2 See yesterday's game with your very own, apparently (4)
3 Offside snare (4)
4 Italian club which might be called Bury in a Thesaurus (5)
5 1980/90s United goalkeeper (3, 6)
6 Billy – – – – – –, 1920s United full-back sinned backwards! (anag) (6)
9 Were Charlton, Best & Edwards tsars (anag) (5)
11 Alex Ferguson has been acclaimed – – – – – – – – – the Month many times (7, 2)
13 Initially Cole, Ince & Albiston hide US federal bureau (3)
15 Nickname of club striker Teddy Sheringham joined from United in 2001 (5)
16 Help to score a goal (6)
18 Road where Louis Saha was at home (temporary) before moving to Old Trafford (6)
19 Country where Paul Ince moved to and Juan Veron arrived from (5)
21 – – – – Coton, 1990s goalkeeper signed from across the city (4)
22 Penalty outcome in Fabien Barthez's favour (4)

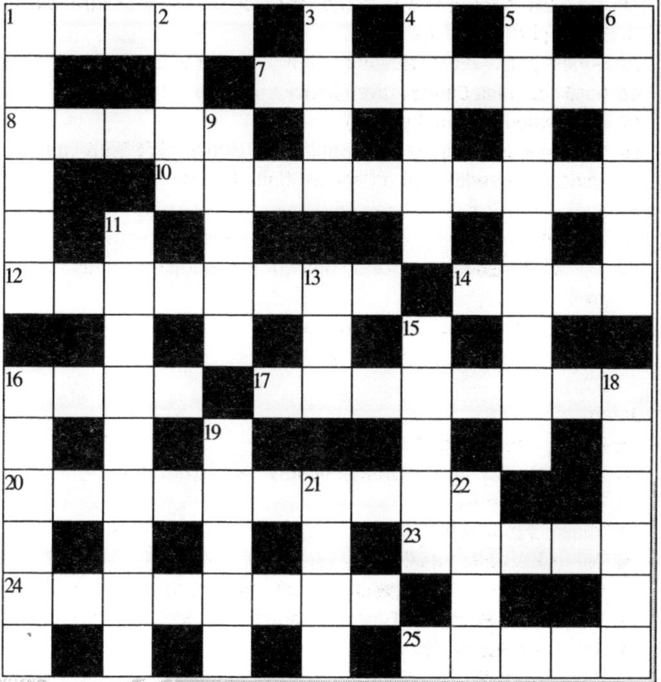

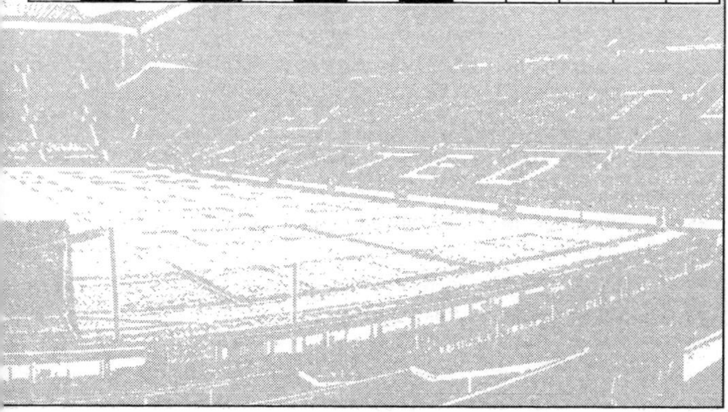

## Across

**6** Hurt llama ran to find 1910s United full-back (anag) (6, 6)

**8** Now more commonly called tie-ups, they support football socks (7)

**9** – – – – – back not left though! (5)

**10** – – – – Cantona, 1990s Old Trafford legend (4)

**12** – – – Alex Ferguson – – –, full title (3, 3)

**14** Shirt number that passed from *10 across* to David Beckham to Christiano Ronaldo (5)

**15** East – – – – – –, English region home to club beaten 9–0 at Old Trafford in 1995 (6)

**16** Part of the body used for scoring not the foot though! (4)

**19** Important happening at Old Trafford (5)

**21** FA Cup runners-up in 1985 (7)

**22** Bobby Charlton retired in the year nineteen – – – – – – – – – – – – (7, 5)

## Down

**1** Appearing at Old Trafford like football celebrities do (8)

**2** The Laws of the Game are often inaccurately called these (5)

**3** Gary, 1980s/90s United goalkeeper (5)

**4** Nil rack reveals *18 down* forward, John (anag) (7)

**5** Every club likes to start season with a big – – – – (4)

**6** Goal calculations in European matches, perhaps! (10)

**7** Match crowd figure (10)

**11** Hot drink hides in football team, apparently (3)

**12** Ex-Reds Maurice Setters hides tennis term, apparently (3)

**13** The cress reveals former United goalkeeper, Arthur (anag) (8)

**14** Shirt number of Roy Keane in 2003–04 (7)

**17** – – – – – Gillespie, United forward 1992/95 (5)

**18** Manchester United were formerly called Newton – – – – – (5)

**20** One all is not an odd score (4)

## Across

**3** Clean farm reveals 1950s United forward, Noel (anag) (9)

**8** Eventually the match finishes level, apparently (4)

**9** Billy Meredith was not the latest superstar! (8)

**10** 2000s United keeper Tim Howard hails from the United
– – – – – – of America (6)

**13** John – – – – –, 1960s Reds winger (5)

**14** Danny – – – – – – –, 1980s/90s United striker (7)

**15** – – – Atkinson, United boss 1981–86 (3)

**16** United were knocked out by North End club when the FA Cup
was a two-legged competition in 1946 (7)

**17** Imprinted club emblem, perhaps! (5)

**21** – – – – – – Quixall, 1950s/60s United forward (6)

**22** Equalising goal (8)

**23** – – – – Davies, 1980s United and Wales winger (4)

**24** Easy targets (4, 5)

## Down

**1** 1980s/90s, Reds left-sided forward (3, 6)

**2** Cup games can be decided on these (9)

**4** Man– – – – –er United Football Club (5)

**5** Quinton Fortune, South – – – – – – – born 1990s/2000s United
forward (7)

**6** Ex-United striker Brian McClair hides a wild animal's resting
place, apparently (4)

**7** Oft-broken facial feature of defender Steve Bruce (4)

**11** Oriel land reveals 2000s United squad forward, Daniel (anag) (9)

**12** Choosing the team from squad (9)

**14** United last – – – the Champions League 1999 (3)

**15** Cristiano – – – – – – –, 2000s United & Portugal midfielder (7)

**18** – – – – – Poborsky, Czech 1990s Republic and United forward (5)

**19** Assist with goal (4)

**20** Alter lane for thin goalscoring spell (anag) (4)

## Across

**1** Not a right-sided player if they are, perhaps! (4-6)

**8** Champions League rivals in 2003 version of the Battle of Britain (7)

**9** Reject drunk & disorderly fan from ground, apparently (5)

**10** – – – – Duxbury, 1980s/90s United defender (4)

**11** Henning – – – –, 1990s United & Norway defender (4)

**12** How Bobby Charlton and Alex Ferguson should be addressed (3)

**14** Get a haircut from 1920s United forward, Jack, but not *16 down*, Mr Tod (6)

**15** Say ram for Newton Heath half-back, Robert (anag) (6)

**18** Coventry City attempt to beat United, apparenty (3)

**20** Mates of Derby County fans found in the West Stand, apparently (4)

**21** Ex-United keeper Barthez erodes a goalless number, apparently (4)

**23** United travelled to Brazil to play in the 2000 FIFA – – – – – Club Championship (5)

**24** The man who used to treat injured players (7)

**25** Type of incident for which a referee should immediately stop play! (4, 6)

## Down

**1** Gary – – – – – – –, was one goal short of Bobby Charlton's England goalscoring record (7)

**2** – – – – Erentz Newton Heath full-back not Harry though! (4)

**3** Fisherman conceals Newton Heath forward James, apparently (6)

**4** Vacant target for striker (4, 4)

**5** Match odds for level game (5)

**6** Old Trafford for United & Blundell Park for – – – – – – – – – – – (7, 4)

**7** Ian – – – – – – – – – – – –, 1970s United forward (6-5)

**13** 1990s/2000s, United brothers Gary & Phil Neville protected the United goal (8)

**16** 1970s TV cop series or 1920s/30s United forward, Eric (7)

**17** Dave – – – – – –, United manager 1977–81 (6)

**19** Dwight – – – – –, 1990s United and Trinidad striker (5)

**22** Not a female term when mentioning the Old Trafford team (3, 1)

**Across**

**1** Ex-United full-back – – – – – Linkson has no scar, apparently (5)
**4** Wes – – – – –, 1990s/2000s United and England defender (5)
**10** – – – – – Warsaw, Polish opponents in 1991 Cup-winners Cup semi-final (5)
**11** Crowd misbehaviour (7)
**12** First leg score in United's favour when they played *10 across* (5, 3)
**13** United player is a Red Devil, Mansfield Town player is a – – – – (4)
**15** – – – – – – Scanlon, United forward 1954/61 (6)
**17** Competition for places can be – – – – – – at Old Trafford at times (6)
**19** Unfair challenge (4)
**20** – – – – – – – – – Adams married United and England hero David Beckham (8)
**23** Itchier 1970/80s United forward, Andy (anag) (7)
**24** Alter football trial when on the right course (anag) (5)
**25** Unclean game reveals family member, apparently (5)
**26** Not the best performance for George Best, maybe! (5)

**Down**

**2** Agars reveals ex-United forward, Charlie (anag) (5)
**3** Non professional players (8)
**5** It's raised at the Millennium Stadium (4)
**6** Colin – – – – – – –, 1950s United & Wales international (7)
**7** Home of Manchester United Football Club (3, 8)
**8** The Stretford End is one at *7 down* (5)
**9** Furniture item for football division (6, 5)
**14** Year of the first title for Busby Babes – – – – – – – – (5, 3)
**16** Park here when Harry Gregg managed Carlisle United 1986–87 (7)
**18** Goes down for the ball like 2000s Tim Howard does, perhaps (5)
**21** Not streets when United play at Elland & Portman (5)
**22** – – – – Neville, 1990s/2000s United defender (4)

## Across

**1** Michael – – – – – – – scored Bayer Leverkusen's first goal in the 2002 Champions League semi-final (7)

**7** Busby – – – – – (5)

**8** The ref would call off a game with a band on the pitch, apparently! (7)

**9** Lee – – – – – –, 1980s/90s United forward joined from Torquay (6)

**11** Snatches the title with Peter Schmeichel's hands, maybe! (5)

**13** Replaces marksmen with playing cards, apparently (4)

**14** – – – – – – – Blanc, 2000s United French born defender (7)

**15** Take a tumble like ex-Newton Heath goalkeeper, Joe (4)

**16** Strong weather hazards can make ball unpredictable (5)

**17** – – – – – – Cup, name by which the 2004 Carling competition was originally known (6)

**21** One in football four in a year (7)

**22** Johnny – – – – –, Footballer of the Year 1949 (5)

**23** Test a player's stamina (7)

## Down

**2** Change paper table for ex-United forward (anag) (6, 4)

**3** Direct style of football much derided by purists (4-4)

**4** Axe a manager (4)

**5** Red carded and a player faces an early – – – – (4)

**6** 1970s/80s forward Stuart Pearson hides a fruit, apparently (4)

**9** Type of European Cup contested by Champions League and UEFA Cup winners (5)

**10** Positions for top FIFA job (10)

**12** Line formed at Old Trafford turnstile (5)

**13** Ron – – – – – – – –, United boss 1981–86 (8)

**18** – – – – Tate, 2000s United squad defender (4)

**19** Employs the ball (4)

**20** – – – – -final, the penultimate round (4)

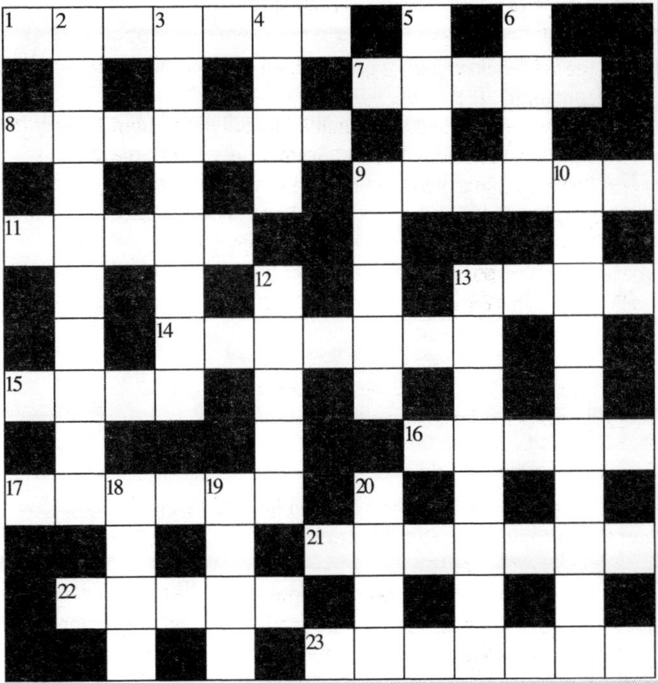
1
2
3
4
5
6
7
8
9
10
11
12
13
14
15
16
17
18
19
20
21
22
23

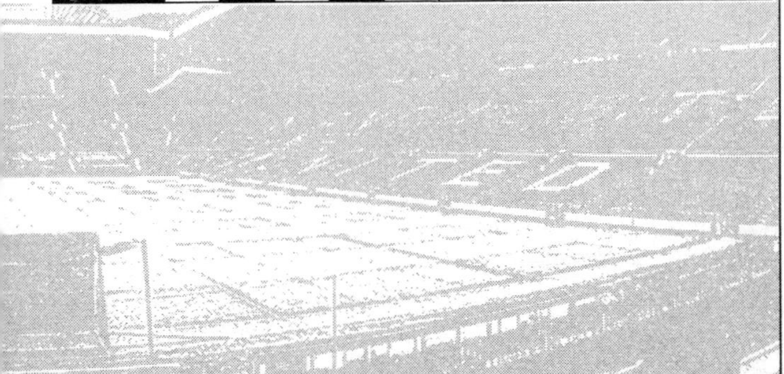

## Across

**1** Nickname of club Teddy Sheringham left to join *3 down* in 1997 (5)

**7** Type of game when each team has one player sent-off (3-1-4)

**8** Ascend the table (5)

**10** Festal draw for ex-United goalkeeper (anag) (3, 7)

**12** Led nylon reveals Newton Heath forward (anag) (10)

**14** Unobstructed points of – – – – at Old Trafford (4)

**16** Away goals counting double is a competition – – – –, not a football law (4)

**17** Challenges for the ball in football competition (8)

**20** Serious – – – – – – – – – – – is an automatic red card offence (10)

**23** Not a late goal (5)

**24** They must be covered or removed before players play (8)

**25** High temperature a United cup run may bring (5)

## Down

**1** Runner-up spot in Premiership (6)

**2** How a native would spell the city Juan Sebastian Veron left to join United (4)

**3** Coloured nickname for United (4)

**4** Creates a goal (5)

**5** Manchester United and Benfica were this in the 1968 European Cup (9)

**6** Odd web makes ex-United forward, John (anag) (6)

**9** Juan Sebastian Veron left the Reds for the – – – – – in 2003 (5)

**11** Part of ground for crowd (9)

**13** Star sign of 1990s/2000s midfielder Roy Keane (3)

**15** Posh – – – – – married ex-United midfielder, David Beckham (5)

**16** Alex Stepney's deputy goalkeeper, Jimmy – – – – – – (6)

**18** Wry sea reveals Newton Heath forward (anag) (6)

**19** United forward Mark – – – – –s joined Norwich City 1992 (5)

**21** Shovels the ball out of the net (4)

**22** Domesticated team (anag) (4)

## Across

**6** United beat Liverpool 2–1 in nineteen – – – – – – – – – – – – FA Cup final (7, 5)

**8** Ex-United forward Andrei Kanchelskis originated from this European area (7)

**9** Wireless for listen to football commentary (5)

**10** Not a low ball (4)

**12** Bryan – – – – – –, Captain Marvel (6)

**14** Steve Bruce managed this Athletic club 2001 (5)

**15** Athletic side United beat in 1994 FA Cup semi-final (6)

**16** Paul – – – –, 1990s United midfielder (4)

**19** David – – – – –, ex-United forward not 1990s/2000s Villa chairman, Doug (5)

**21** Nationality of 1990s/2000s United forward Jesper Blomqvist (7)

**22** 1960s/70s, United & Scotland international winger (6, 6)

## Down

**1** For England United's Tommy Taylor – – – – – – – – a goal every 106 minutes (8)

**2** Unite laces when removing them from boots (anag) (5)

**3** Martin – – – – –, English football commentator (5)

**4** Stuart – – – – – – –, 1970s United forward nicknamed Pancho (7)

**5** David – – – –, 1960s goalscoring United star (4)

**6** Country who jointly hosted 2002 World Cup (5, 5)

**7** 1940s/50s, United keeper known as Sonny (4, 6)

**11** – – – Howard, 2000s United goalkeeper (3)

**12** – – – Wilkins, 1970s/80s United & England captain (3)

**13** Into saga reveals the – – – – – – – – Bernabeu stadium (anag) (8)

**14** Side nicknamed the Saddlers not 1960s/70s United midfielder David Sadler though! (7)

**17** Is Les Olive surrounded by bodies of water (5)

**18** English county where Lee Sharpe was a trainee with Torquay United (5)

**20** Passed on a chance as a hen did to an egg (4)

## Across

**3** Advertising United merchandise, perhaps! (9)

**8** In 1991, Nobby Stiles was the subject on TV's *This is – – – – Life* (4)

**9** Dublin born 1960s United goalkeeper (3, 5)

**10** Oil pan will reveal Italian side based in Naples (anag) (6)

**13** Scottish stadium where Alex Ferguson turned out as a player (5)

**14** Soccer umpire, perhaps! (7)

**15** *23 across* and *12 down* also played for – – –castle United (3)

**16** 1961 season David Herd was pipped by Jimmy – – – – – – – for top Division One scorer (7)

**17** Tom – – – – –, 1910s United forward who enjoyed home respect, apparently (5)

**21** 2000s, United goalkeeper Tim Howard hails from the United – – – – – – of America (6)

**22** Ex-United striker Frank Stapleton gained 71 – – – – – – – – of Ireland caps (8)

**23** Andy – – – –, prolific 1990s United goalscorer (4)

**24** Chelsea defender & England team mate of United's Gary Neville (4, 5)

## Down

**1** 1990s/2000s Welshman was the youngest-ever United player to gain a full international cap (4, 5)

**2** United fan (9)

**4** Schmeichel made a wonder save against – – – – – Vienna in 1996 (5)

**5** – – – – – – – Williams, forward who turned pro at United in 2000 (7)

**6** Rout turns into pre-season travelling friendly (anag) (4)

**7** Shirt number for United legend Bobby Charlton (4)

**11** Method of gaining entry to the English Premiership (9)

**12** Peter – – – – – – – – – –, 1980s England striker only played once for United (9)

**14** Result or reserve (short) (3)

**15** Gary – – – – – – –, 1990s/2000s United defender (7)

**18** Acting award for divers in the penalty area (5)

**19** United's George Best was – – – – –worshipped by millions (4)

**20** In rotation system take yours to play (4)

|1| |2| |3|4| |5| |6| |7| |
|8| | | | | | | | | | | | |
| | | | |9| | | | | | | | |
|10| | | | | | | | | | | | |
| | | | | | | | | |11| |12| |
|13| | | | |14| | | | | | | |
| | | | |15| | | | | | | | |
|16| | | | | | |17| | | | | |
| | | | | |18| | | | | | | |
| |19| |20| | |21| | | | | | |
|22| | | | | | | | | | | | |
| | | | | | | |23| | | | | |
|24| | | | | | | | | | | | |

## Across

**1** Bryan Robson signed for United from – – – – Bromwich – – – – – – in 1981 (4, 6)

**8** Nickname of club which knocked out United from FA Cup at Vicarage Road in 1982 (7)

**9** Capital Italian Serie A side, former home of Juan Veron (5)

**10** They think it's all over – – – – now (2, 2)

**11** Amount of times Peter Beardsley played for United (4)

**12** Initially a distress call for Solskjaer, O'Shea & Sheringham (3)

**14** Ex-United striker Ted MacDougall was a – – – – – before becoming a Devil (6)

**15** Chris – – – – – –, 1980s United goalkeeper (6)

**18** Player on bench (short) (3)

**20** 1970s United forward Gordon Hill was best on left side (4)

**21** – – – – Djemba-Djemba, 2000s United midfielder (4)

**23** – – – – – West, ex-United forward known as Knocker (5)

**24** Nationality of Denis Law's Torino team mates, maybe! (7)

**25** Position United finished in Division One 1989–90 season (10)

## Down

**1** 1930s/40s, during – – – – – – – years football was suspended at Old Trafford (7)

**2** John O'– – – –, United defender (4)

**3** – – – – – – Wenger, 2004 title winning manager (6)

**4** Stadium in Manchester but not for football though! (5, 3)

**5** When on-form a United player – – – – – confidence (5)

**6** Parch crises for 1990s United defender (anag) (5, 6)

**7** Equestrian hobby for Bryan Robson and Alex Ferguson, perhaps! (5, 6)

**13** Stan – – – – – – – –, 1950s United defender signed 1 hour before his debut (8)

**16** Steve Bruce turned professional at this club 1978 (7)

**17** Clearly in team and not offside (6)

**19** Kiosk or Newton Heath forward, William (5)

**22** Herbert, 1930s United forward not ex-Germany striker Jurgen Klins– – – – – (4)

## Across

1 Title winning United player (short) (5)
4 Sir - - - - - Charlton, legendary United forward (5)
10 Winner reveals type of circle, apparently (5)
11 Goal ratio (7)
12 Jim, United goalkeeper 1988/90 & Scotland international (8)
13 Alex Ferguson once managed - - - - Stirlingshire (4)
15 Tommy - - - - - -, St Helens born 1970s United full-back (6)
17 Mike - - - - - -, 1980s/90s United utility player (6)
19 Team selection sheet (4)
20 1950s United goalkeeper (3, 5)
23 Poked with arm joint (7)
24 Oliver may have to when going through turnstile (5)
25 United's Lee Sharpe won - - - - - Player of the Year 1991 (5)
26 Undergarments often revealed in goal celebrations (5)

## Down

2 Benfica's 1968 European Cup goalkeeper was - - - - -que (5)
3 Arms hall reveals Liverpool born ex-United full-back, Arthur (anag) (8)
5 Type of target when 2000s Mark Bosnich was missing from goal (4)
6 Sheffield Lane where United's 1993 FA Cup dreams ended (7)
7 Only Bobby Charlton has made more United appearances than this defender (4, 6)
8 - - - - - Ground, Oxford, the venue of Alex Ferguson's first game in charge of Manchester United (5)
9 Former name of Manchester United (6, 5)
14 Before becoming a Devil Bryan Robson was not just a Baggie (8)
16 Legendary Benfica striker played in 1968 European Cup Final (7)
18 Not tails for choice of ends (5)
21 Moronic term for football hooligan (5)
22 Although brothers Jack was not Bobby Charlton's - - - - (4)

**Across**

 1 Matt Busby was Great Britain's coach at these 1948 Games (7)
 7 Match hold up (5)
 8 Roy − − − − − − −, 2000s United goalkeeper (7)
 9 George, ex-United defender nicknamed Silent (6)
 11 − − − − − Cruyff, 1990s United midfielder (5)
 13 − − − − Beardsmore, United midfielder joined AFC Bournemouth 1993 (short) (4)
 14 Spectators stand (7)
 15 Old Trafford for United & − − −bury for Arsenal (4)
 16 Roy − − − − −, United and Republic of Ireland midfielder (5)
 17 Score of FA Cup semi-final, United v Oldham, in 1994 (3, 3)
 21 Penalty pleas (7)
 22 − − − − − Robson, left United for Middlesbrough 1994 (5)
 23 United were playing − − − − − − − Palace when Eric Cantona jumped into the crowd (7)

**Down**

 2 − − − − -'− − − − − −, 1980s United and Republic of Ireland midfielder (4, 1'5)
 3 Billy, United's oldest international of all time (8)
 4 Lazy football idol say! (4)
 5 George − − − −, scored 6 goals in 8–2 win against Northampton Town 1970 (4)
 6 − − − − Astrid, where United played their first ever European tie (4)
 9 Number of players a team is selected from (5)
 10 Area for ex-United forward Alan Brazil when playing for Ipswich Town (4, 6)
 12 Reward or honour for football victory (5)
 13 Match judges (8)
 18 Gaelic name for national side of *16 across* (4)
 19 Tidy play (4)
 20 Teddy Sheringham was transferred to Tottenham Hot− − − − (4)

## Across

**1** Time is – – – – on for injuries, maybe! (5)

**7** Alter each hold for 1920S United forward, Arthur (anag) (8)

**8** Alter roots for when 1990s United team ruled the – – – – – (anag) (5)

**10** I shared MOT around to find United's leading goalscorer in 1930–31 relegation season (anag) (6, 4)

**12** Michael – – – – – – – –, United midfielder 1996–97 (8)

**14** Soccer louts aren't really confused boys (anag) (4)

**16** Dressing space to get changed (4)

**17** Ron Atkinson managed this club on two separate occasions (shortened) (4, 4)

**20** Jules Rimet and Stanley Rous held these FIFA positions (10)

**23** Time Arthur Albiston revealed planet, apparently (5)

**24** Striker such as 1990s/2000s Reds star Ole Gunnar Solskjaer (8)

**25** He ban 1930s United & Republic of Ireland goalkeeper, Billy (anag) (5)

## Down

**1** 1990s/2000s United midfielder Quinton Fortune was born in South – – – – – – (6)

**2** Ex-United midfielder Paul Ince was an – – – – End boy (4)

**3** Boo Man City during a prosperous time, apparently (4)

**4** Man– – – – –er United Football Club (5)

**5** United's Dutch opponents in 1997–98 Champions League (9)

**6** German sportswear giants produced United kits 1980s/90s (6)

**9** Put the ball into play using hands (5)

**11** United's match competitors (9)

**13** Number for 2000s United goalkeeper Fabien Barthez (3)

**15** Condition of ground, perhaps! (5)

**16** Drawn cup match goes to a player (anag) (6)

**18** Nee ham makes ex-United half-back, Tommy (anag) (6)

**19** Cricket or football field (5)

**21** Seven goals are not that odd, apparently (4)

**22** Out of danger regarding relegation (4)

## Across

6 United winger 1975/83 (5, 7)
8 Sepp – – – – – – –, 1990s/2000s FIFA president (7)
9 Bird of prey for 2000s United midfielder Chris (5)
10 1990s United and Denmark goalkeeper Peter Schmeichel stands 6feet 4inches – – – – (4)
12 Alerts to this Newton Heath goalkeeper (anag) (6)
14 Alex Bell is able to find a 1920s forward, David, apparently (5)
15 In 1892 Newton Heath defeated Wolves – – – – – – (3, 3)
16 Type of dead ball kick (4)
19 Soccer test for youngsters (5)
21 Games behind closed doors are held in – – – – – – – – (7)
22 Inch theft & jot reveals ex-United defender (anag) (4, 8)

## Down

1 Allergen reveals London born 1950s United goalkeeper (anag) (3, 5)
2 Whips the opposition (5)
3 Ian Storey– – – – –, 1970s United forward (5)
4 Disputes match ban, maybe! (7)
5 Carried by assistant referee (4)
6 Player on stand-by (10)
7 1960s/70s United legend (6, 4)
11 – – – Gunnar Solskjaer, 1990s/2000s United striker (3)
12 At the County Ground in 1970, 7 *down* hit Northampton Town for this (3)
13 Standing ground features (8)
14 Bobby Charlton scored a record 49 goals for this country (7)
17 Penultimate month for the English football season (5)
18 Surface for playing football (5)
20 I Ronaldo can press forward for creased United shirts, apparently (4)

## Across

3 Scored for United in 1968 European Cup Final victory (5, 4)
8 Part of the body for 1920s United forward Arthur Lochhead, apparently (4)
9 Not a direct free-kick (8)
10 United have forgotten Don Givens had sinew problems, apparently (6)
13 Some goalkeepers have - - - - - hands than others (5)
14 Cash men reveal 1950s United forward, Harry (anag) (7)
15 - - - Athens, capital Greek League side (1,1,1)
16 Raimond Van - - - - - - -, 1990s/2000s United goalkeeper (3, 4)
17 Confronted the opposition head on! (5)
21 Jimmy - - - - - -, 1930s/40s United forward (6)
22 - - - - - - - - Beckham, Posh Spice (8)
23 A non-league side is starting soon, apparently (4)
24 Showed off silverware in case at Old Trafford (9)

## Down

1 Norman - - - - - - - - -, Belfast-born 1980s United forward (9)
2 No hard fan for 1920s United forward Charlie (anag) (9)
4 Pours down when player trains, apparently (5)
5 Newton Heath's rivals later called Manchester City (7)
6 - - - - Hilton, 2000s United squad defender (4)
7 - - - - Peqq, 1900s United forward, but not author Mr Francis! (4)
11 Legendary Reds striker Mark Hughes joined this Spanish club 1986 (9)
12 Rio - - - - - - - - -, 2000s United defender (9)
14 Jack - - -, United goalkeeper 1910s/20s (3)
15 Country for previous United opponents Rapid Vienna (7)
18 Divide the points in drawn match (5)
19 Subs can often pay - - - -dends for club shareholders (4)
20 Halt play by the post (anag) (4)

## Across

**1** --- ---- Busby ---, full knighted title (3, 4, 3)
**8** Bobby Charlton's brother managed this Republic country (7)
**9** Bobby Charlton played his last game for United in the ------ Italian tournament (5)
**10** Brian ----, 1990s assistant United manager (4)
**11** Nickname of Scottish team Alex Ferguson played for not Queens Park though! (4)
**12** ----league football is not top flight (3)
**14** ------ Muhren, Dutch born 1980s United midfielder (6)
**15** Joe -----, managed Man City when Sir Matt Busby managed United (6)
**18** --- Lynam, TV football presenter (3)
**20** Drop from Italian side, apparently (4)
**21** ---- Parker, 1990s United and England defender (4)
**23** Draw level with another player's record (5)
**24** Goal surround (7)
**25** Ruud van ----------, 2000s United striker (10)

## Down

**1** Len dosh reveals ex-United forward John (anag) (7)
**2** ---- Giggs, 1990s/2000s United & Wales forward (4)
**3** Formal name by which 1990s/2000s forward Mr Cole wished to be known (6)
**4** Request this kind of move (8)
**5** Tommy -----, Scottish born 1940s/50s United forward (5)
**6** Cranked grid reveals ex-United forward (anag) (4, 7)
**7** Soccer pitch features (6, 5)
**13** Dark night games have to be for visibility (8)
**16** In 1997 United beat Chelsea 4 in the FA ------- Shield (7)
**17** Cup result which means it goes to penalties (3, 3)
**19** ----- Arabia, participated in 1998 World Cup Finals (5)
**22** Shoot Tony Coton to reveal German forename, apparently (4)

## Across

1 Club premises for selling merchandise (5)
4 The - - - - -, former United training ground (5)
10 United player yearns for his football wages, apparently (5)
11 Gain ere reveals African Nations team (anag) (7)
12 Capital term for 1990s/2000s United forward Teddy Sheringham (8)
13 Gordon - - - -, United winger arrived from Millwall 1975 (4)
15 Norman Whiteside hides colours, apparently (6)
17 Forename of 1990s United forward, Mr Kanchelskis (6)
19 Nights before many FA Cup Finals (4)
20 Perpetrator of foul (8)
23 Arch lie reveals Mr Roberts, 1900s/10s United captain (anag) (7)
24 Advance to find Newton Heath forward James, apparently (5)
25 Posh Spice's maiden name (5)
26 Nickname of the side Steve Bruce managed 2000s (5)

## Down

2 Wading bird or 1950s/60s United forward, Tommy (5)
3 On paper a very easy game for United (8)
5 European fixtures involving two limbs (4)
6 Fire err for 1930s United forward (anag) (7)
7 El new cereal for 2004 United squad defender (3, 9)
8 Paul Ince played for this Italian international side (5)
9 Nearly tie up 2000s United squad midfielder (anag) (4, 7)
14 Half-time break (8)
16 Lee Sharpe signed to play in this country 2003 (7)
18 Player bid (5)
21 Nobby Stiles did a jig at Wembley after winning 1966 World Cup (5)
22 Fruity cup tie when teams get United (4)

**Across**

1 Newton Heath beat - - - - - - - Town Swifts 14–0 in 1895 (7)
7 Half-time interval (5)
8 Paul - - - - - - -, 1980s United & Republic of Ireland defender (7)
9 - - - - - - Carey, 1930s/40s/50s legendary United skipper (6)
11 Set move (5)
13 2000s Alex Ferguson for United, - - - - Dowie for Crystal Palace (4)
14 Saintly ground Steve Bruce went to as manager 2001 (7)
15 - - - - Pearson, scored winning 1948 FA Cup winning goal (4)
16 Football contest (5)
17 Harm yourself in challenge (6)
21 Saudi - - - - - - - players took part in World Cup 1998 (7)
22 Yen pa makes ex-United forward, Ernest (anag) (5)
23 Erik - - - - - - -, 1990s/2000s United & Norway forward (7)

**Down**

2 - - - - - - - - - - Stanley played United 1945–46 FA Cup tie (10)
3 Gordon - - - - - - - -, United midfielder joined Leeds in 1989 (8)
4 Not an early kick-off (4)
5 Beat Rio Ferdinand to the treble, apparently (4)
6 1980s, United forward Peter Barnes hides farm building, apparently (4)
9 Mark - - - - -, Busby Babe who perished at Munich (5)
10 Inane climb reveals ex-United half-back (anag) (4, 6)
12 - - - - Colman, Busby Babe half-back (5)
13 City where Galatasaray knocked out United in 1993–94 European Cup (8)
18 - - - - Veron, former United midfielder (4)
19 Call ex-United forward Teddy Sheringham, apparently (4)
20 No cost for this kick (4)

## Across

**1** Soccer teams (5)
**7** Soccer match at Old Trafford (4, 4)
**8** Paul Ince's star sign (5)
**10** United's 1998–99 Champions League quarter final opponents (5, 5)
**12** Elm cents reveal Newton Heath full-back, John (anag) (8)
**14** It confuses the defence when striker employs the ball, apparently (4)
**16** Bryan Robson joined United from – – – – Bromwich Albion 1981 (4)
**17** Number of managers United had before Alex Ferguson (8)
**20** Type of domestic non-cup match (6, 4)
**23** Fussy referee wants ball placed on the precise spot (5)
**24** Not mornings or afternoons for kick-offs (8)
**25** Alex Ferguson succeeded Jock – – – – – as Scottish manager in a caretaker capacity (5)

## Down

**1** Scottish club who were opponents for Bobby Charlton's testimonial in 1972 (6)
**2** Trainee United midfielder David Platt played for this Italian side (4)
**3** Ronnie – – – –, 1950s/60s Reds half-back (4)
**4** Mates make football sides (anag) (5)
**5** Gary – – – – – – – – –, partnered Steve Bruce in defence for seven years (9)
**6** Forename of 1950s/60s United forward, Mr Viollet (6)
**9** Can German side annoy United, apparently (5)
**11** United headlines are placed in here, maybe! (9)
**13** One goal short of hat-trick (3)
**15** Ex-United midfielder or defender Ashley Grimes hides soot, apparently (5)
**16** Nickname of club where Paul Ince and Denis Irwin played in 2003–04 (6)
**18** United's previous name was – – – – – – Heath (6)
**19** Italian city where Denis Law played (5)
**21** Bury's Lane is home to Ryan Giggs, perhaps! (4)
**22** Way out at football ground (4)

**Across**

6 Very real arch for ex-United forward (anag) (5, 7)
8 Every player has eventually - - - - - - - (7)
9 Star sign of 2000s United goalkeeper, Roy Carroll (5)
10 Does Sir Alex Ferguson constantly - - - - gum? (4)
12 - - - - - - Anderson, United forward 1970s (6)
14 Leeds Utd manager when Sir Matt Busby was managing United (5)
15 People in charge of United (6)
16 Corner - - - - (4)
19 - - - - - Bond, 1950s United forward (5)
21 Saintly French side United played in 1977 (7)
22 Filing billed reveals United 1940s/50s goalkeeper (anag) (4, 8)

**Down**

1 Relationship between 1990s/2000s United players Phil & Gary (8)
2 Joe - - - - - -cough, 1920s United forward (5)
3 Leaf from grass pitch at Bramall Lane (nick) (5)
4 Not a success after high transfer expectations (7)
5 Neil - - - -, 1989/93 United midfielder, the 1000th player to be capped for England (4)
6 Reach below to find ex-United full-back (anag) (6, 4)
7 1950s/60s, Northern Ireland & United goalkeeper (5, 5)
11 - - - Sealey, 1990s United goalkeeper (3)
12 - - - Howard, 2000s United goalkeeper (3)
13 Spanish side knocked-out United in UEFA Cup 1982–83 season (8)
14 Alter leavers when manager shows his team at the very last minute (anag) (7)
17 Forename of United forward whose autobiography was called *The Lawman* (5)
18 Paul McGrath left United for Aston - - - - - 1989 (5)
20 - - - - McBain, 1920s United midfielder who, in 1947, became the oldest man ever to appear in the Football League (4)

## Across

3 1990s/2000s, United players Andy Cole & Ruud van Nistlerooy (9)

8 Dave Sexton was manager at QPR's Loftus – – – – 1974–77 (4)

9 1970s United defender Brian Greenhoff also played for this Spotland club (8)

10 Football in general (6)

13 – – – – – McClair, scored the last goal of the 1994 FA Cup Final (5)

14 Leo jade reveals 1940s United forward (anag) (3, 4)

15 Spanish sun can be found at the heart of the England defence (3)

16 Person in charge of match (7)

17 Nationality of United legend Billy Meredith (5)

21 Forest warden for Queens Park Rangers player, apparently (6)

22 Leech ore for 2000s United defender (anag) (3, 5)

23 – – – – Scholes, 1990s/2000s United and England midfielder (4)

24 Tennis bar makes 1906–10 United forward, Jimmy (anag) (9)

## Down

1 They form part of the woodwork (9)

2 Fired calf reveals Newton Heath forward, George (anag) (9)

4 – – – – – Cooke, United forward 1995 (5)

5 Type of drink banned from some football stadiums (7)

6 Brian – – – –, ex-United striker & Blackburn boss 1998–99 (4)

7 Reds captain Roy Keane is great in a ball-winning midfield one (4)

11 Opening score is not late (5, 4)

12 Well there you go to find Newton Heath player, Joe (anag) (9)

14 – – – Jordan, 1970s/80s United & Scotland forward known as "Jaws" (3)

15 Picks the side (7)

18 Dennis Viollet coached at this Alexandra club (5)

19 United reached the – – – – Cup quarter-finals in 1984–85 (4)

20 Ex-United midfielder Carlo Sartori ran off to the Middle East, apparently (4)

## Across

1 Final scores over two legs (10)
8 Match official (7)
9 – – – – – Forlan, 2000s United & Uruguay striker (5)
10 A Viv Anderson pass reveals Israeli capital side Tel – – – –, apparently (4)
11 Penalty taker reveals Newton Heath forward, Hugh (4)
12 Relationship of 1990s midfielder Darren Ferguson to United boss, apparently (3)
14 Soccer outcome (6)
15 1990s/2000s United defender Ronny Johnsen's native country (6)
18 – – – Murray, 1930s United forward (short) (3)
20 Away match for United's following fans (4)
21 – – – – Phelan, 1980s/90s United utility player (4)
23 Roma ghetto reveals the headquarters of a County Tyrone branch of United Supporters Club, apparently (5)
24 Rent art for 1963–64 United half-back, Wilf (anag) (7)
25 Goose verge reveals 1930s/40s United half-back (anag) (6, 4)

## Down

1 Business happenings at Old Trafford, perhaps (7)
2 – – – – Neville, 1990s/2000s United defender (4)
3 Number of players in starting line-up (6)
4 Viv – – – – – – – –, 1980s/90s United & England full-back (8)
5 Odds for equal games (5)
6 1980s/90s United & England midfielder and captain (5, 6)
7 1950s United forward (6, 5)
13 Darren – – – – – – – –, 2000s United midfielder (8)
16 Carried by 8 across (7)
17 Brian – – – – – –, succeeded Ron Atkinson aT Aston Villa in 1994 (6)
19 Couple of goals (5)
22 No holy circle for Red Devil player (4)

## Across

**1** Found on the sole of football boots (5)

**4** Soccer fixture (5)

**10** Ex-United defender Kevin Moran ticks off a player prank, apparently (5)

**11** Goals conceded from opposition (7)

**12** In 2004, United won the FA Cup for the – – – – – – – – time (8)

**13** Rochdale nickname or 1940s United forward, Joe (4)

**15** Flood– – – – – – brighten up Old Trafford (6)

**17** Striker Brian McClair signed from this Scottish side in 1987 (6)

**19** 1990s/2000s, United goalkeeper Raimond Van Der – – – – (4)

**20** Drop from Premiership (8)

**23** Marvin – – – – – – –, Millwall defender in 2004 FA Cup final (7)

**24** Ronnie – – – – –, 1940s United forward (5)

**25** George, Newton Heath-born 1930s Reds half-back, not Rotten rocker Johnny though (5)

**26** Given the United's success do the folks at City think this is greener at Old Trafford? (5)

## Down

**2** Name teams strive to win (5)

**3** Tommy – – – – – – – –, United manager 1972–77 (8)

**5** – – – – Gowling, 1960s/70s United forward (4)

**6** 1960s/70s United and England half-back Nobby Stiles wore – – – – – – – lenses (7)

**7** Saturated pitch is! (11)

**8** Sweat time if stalling (anag) (5)

**9** Carried off, perhaps! (11)

**14** Month in which 1990s United goalkeeper Peter Schmeichel was born (8)

**16** Your gal reveals *18 down* half-back, John (anag) (7)

**18** United were formerly called Newton – – – – – (5)

**21** Buenos – – – – –, capital city of country where United lost 1968 World Club Cup (5)

**22** So Lou Macari likes to go alone, apparently (4)

## Across

1 Nationality of United's 1964–65 Inter-City Fairs Cup opponents Djurgaarden (7)

7 – – – – – Davenport, United top goalscorer 1986–87 season (5)

8 Gary – – – – – – –, ex-England striker now TV football presenter (7)

9 Sir can become Newton Heath full-back, James (anag) (6)

11 Nourishes the forwards, perhaps! (5)

13 Go through turnstile when going – – – – the ground (4)

14 First name of central defender signed from Inter in 2001 (7)

15 Month in which 1980s/90s United defender Gary Pallister was born (4)

16 White in France will reveal second name of *14 across* (5)

17 Deep ID for ex-United forward, Jack (anag) (6)

21 Mal – – – – – – –, 1980s/90s United defender also an ex-Gaelic footballer (7)

22 Training settlements where scamps seek peace, apparently (5)

23 Miss eel for 2000s United squad defender (anag) (3, 4)

## Down

2 Coloured dwelling for ex-United goalkeeper, Jimmy (10)

3 Ground where Brian Kidd, Nobby Stiles and Bobby Charlton all managed (8)

4 Ex-United keeper Alex Stepney had to watch his, apparently (4)

5 Alter part of ex-United defender Dave Sadler for Chester City stadium (anag) (4)

6 United strike fright into the opposition, maybe! (4)

9 Ex-United legend nicknamed "Gentleman Johnny" (5)

10 Roy Keane was signed from – – – – – – – – – – Forest in 1993 (10)

12 Pat and Tony – – – – –, 1960s United teammates (5)

13 Nationality of ex-United midfielder Carlo Sartori's countrymen (8)

18 One point for this outcome (4)

19 Manchester United are Red Devils, Lincoln City are Red – – – – (4)

20 Wore alters for one appearance ex-United defender, Josh (anag) (4)

## Across

**1** Dwight Yorke became one at Blackburn in 2003 (5)

**7** England forward who left Old Trafford for Ewood Park in 2001 (4, 4)

**8** David Beckham left England for this country (5)

**10** Con toll men for 1970s United full-back (anag) (3, 7)

**12** 1966 team mate of Nobby Stiles and Bobby Charlton (4, 4)

**14** George Best was a super- - - - (4)

**16** Was 2000s United forward David Bellion greedy, apparently (4)

**17** Modern football formation - - - - - - - -two (4, 4)

**20** Peter - - - - - - - - - -, described as "the world's best goalkeeper" in the 1990s (10)

**23** Taken by writing football managers (5)

**24** Gordon, 1980s United and Scotland midfielder (8)

**25** Sir - - - - - Charlton, United legend (5)

## Down

**1** Country associated with ex-United striker Andrei Kanchelskis not Ukraine though! (6)

**2** Way out at football ground (4)

**3** Initials of side Bobby Charlton managed, 1973–75, - - End - - (4)

**4** No sly will reveal ex-United forward, George (anag) (5)

**5** Born store will reveal ex-United half-back, William (anag) (9)

**6** Roll me reveals 1930s United full-back, Jack (anag) (6)

**9** - - - - - Stiles, 1960s United half-back (5)

**11** 1960s, United forward some people thought was highly underrated (5, 4)

**13** Star sign of ex-United defender Tony Dunne (3)

**15** Colour associated with old style keeper shirts (5)

**16** Help with goal (6)

**18** Sir Alf - - - - - -, England World Cup winning manager (6)

**19** Seat for substitute (5)

**21** Applaud good United performance (4)

**22** Sponsors crest (4)

## Across

**6** Nobby Stiles managed – – – – – – – – – – – End 1977/81 (7, 5)
**8** Caterer for yesterday's Stretford End (anag) (7)
**9** Not a day match (5)
**10** Newton Heath LYR stood for Lancashire & Yorkshire – – – –way (4)
**12** Uriah – – – – – –, 2000s English Premiership referee (6)
**14** English county where United played 1977–78 home Cup winners Cup tie against St Etienne (5)
**15** German side Borussia Dortmund hides a country, apparently (6)
**16** Forename of Mr Cantona or Mr Djemba-Djemba (4)
**19** Cantona's last French club before arriving in England (5)
**21** Andy – – – – – – –, 1970s/80s United forward went on to football management (7)
**22** Run cribs fans for 1960s/70s Reds defender (anag) (7, 5)

## Down

**1** Close goal attempt (4, 4)
**2** Teams reveal vapour (anag) (5)
**3** Shortened version of club Paul Ince left United to join (5)
**4** Ronny – – – – – – –, 1990s/2000s United defender (7)
**5** Bachelor night for Mansfield Town player (nick) (4)
**6** Scottish born 1960s/70s United half-back (3, 7)
**7** Used to carry injured players from the pitch (10)
**11** 1990s United keeper Les Sealey hides the ocean, apparently (3)
**12** – – – Atkinson, United boss 1981–86 (3)
**13** Norman Whiteside's international side was – – – – – – – – Ireland (8)
**14** Bookable offence (7)
**17** Alter cigar for Newton Heath forward (anag) (5)
**18** Soccer ticket attachments (5)
**20** – – – – Hughes, 1980s/90s United and Wales striker (4)

## Across

**3** – – – – – – – – Solskjaer, 1990s/2000s United striker (3, 6)

**8** Eric Cantona was voted Footballer of the – – – – 1996 (4)

**9** Stadium where United lost 2003 Champions League quarter-final first leg (8)

**10** Back of the shirt feature (6)

**13** Home stadium when Alex Ferguson was a player (5)

**14** Clive Thomas or Graham Poll for instance (7)

**15** George Perrins of Newton Heath went so many miles – – – hour, apparently (3)

**16** Nickname of team denied 2003–04 treble by United's FA Cup semi-final win (7)

**17** Soccer aggravation (short) (5)

**21** Duncan – – – – – –s, Busby Babe (6)

**22** United player was one of two in 2003 League Cup Final (8)

**23** – – – – Sexton, United manager 1977/81 (4)

**24** Denis Irwin became Wolverhampton – – – – – – – – – defender 2002 (9)

## Down

**1** Cardiff born 1990s/2000s United forward/midfielder (4, 5)

**2** Inflicting a heavy defeat on West Ham Utd FC, maybe! (9)

**4** Star sign of 2000s United defender, Wes Brown (5)

**5** Grander 1930s United forward, Dick (anag) (7)

**6** Close attempt came – – – – to scoring (4)

**7** – – – – Stepney, United goalkeeper 1960s/70s (4)

**11** Nationality of 2000s United striker, Diego Forlan (9)

**12** Not the first game in European Cup tie (6, 3)

**14** Result or reserve (short) (3)

**15** United were English – – – – – – –ship winners 2003 (7)

**18** – – – – – Schmeichel, 1990s/2000s United goalkeeper (5)

**19** Federation Internationale de Football Association (abbrev) (4)

**20** Six– – – – – box, officially the goal area (4)

## Across

1 Remarry hog for ex-United goalkeeper (anag) (5, 5)
8 Raw roll will show 1940s full-back, Harry (anag) (7)
9 Bird for 2000s United squad midfielder Chris (5)
10 Ex-United goalkeeper Harry Gregg hides a forename, apparently (4)
11 Peterborough United FC's nickname for – – – – Spice (4)
12 – – – Hunter, 1950s United forward (3)
14 United won seven Division One – – – – – – (6)
15 Lancashire side live at Old Trafford, apparently (6)
18 – – – Trafford Stadium (3)
20 – – – – O'Brien, Dublin born United midfielder 1986/89 (4)
21 Peter Schmeichel scored against Rotor Volgograd in United's 1995 – – – – Cup exit (4)
23 – – – – – Moran United midfielder 1978/88 (5)
24 Footballing youngsters may ape their hero's (7)
25 Bobby Charlton managed – – – – – – – North – – – 1973–75 (7, 3)

## Down

1 Forename of 1927/31 United manager, Mr Bamlett (7)
2 Eric Cantona arrived from Elland – – – – in 1992 (4)
3 Colour of caution card (6)
4 1998 Champions League score, Feyenoord – – –, Manchester United – – – – – (3, 5)
5 Freed Gary Neville to find 1990s/2000s Dutch player – – – – Davids, apparently (5)
6 Forward signed from Aston Villa in 1998 (6, 5)
7 Not cup matches (6, 5)
13 Jeffrey – – – – – – – –, 1980s United goalkeeper (8)
16 Johnny Carey captained the Republic of – – – – – – team (7)
17 In Roma you find European minnows San – – – – – (anag) (6)
19 Change drive for a player who receives *3 down* for simulation (anag) (5)
22 United shirt number worn by legend Bill Foulkes in 1968 European Cup Final (4)

## Across

**1** Country where United played for the FIFA Inter-Continental Cup in 1999 (5)

**4** Breach the rules if you get through to the final stage, apparently (5)

**10** Type of oil for 1950s United goalkeeper Les (5)

**11** Rapid Bucharest hail from this country (7)

**12** Use this to ignite a large fire, maybe! (3, 5)

**13** Individual goal not set-piece, perhaps! (4)

**15** Term for football in America (6)

**17** Old and new reveals 1930s United defender, Willie Mc— — — — — (anag) (6)

**19** Is Lee Sharpe surrounded by water, apparently (4)

**20** A move from one club to another (8)

**23** Bobby Charlton gained 106 — — — — — — — caps (7)

**24** Fire the ball at the Gunners (5)

**25** Finish game a point apiece (5)

**26** Nickname of side ex-United defender Viv Anderson managed 1993–94 (5)

## Down

**2** Faxing a manager when sacking them, apparently (5)

**3** Goal statistics, etc (8)

**5** Gem United players hide a girl's name, apparently (4)

**6** Eric — — — — — — —, 1990s France & United maestro (7)

**7** Midfielder who made his Reds debut against Bolton Wanderers 1960 (5, 6)

**8** Hat— — — — —, beats a brace and may earn a match-ball (5)

**9** Old hart bart reveals 1960s United half-back (anag) (6, 5)

**14** Swiss side does not use an older player (5, 3)

**16** One clog reveals German League side (anag) (7)

**18** Liam — — — — —, played against United for Arsenal in the 1979 FA Cup final (5)

**21** Picture surround for 1930s United half-back, Tommy (5)

**22** Back of the shirt titled feature (4)

## Across

1 Noughts & - - - - - - - for football pools coupon or deliveries from the wing (7)
7 - - - - - Robson, ex-United midfielder managed Middlesbrough 1994–2001 (5)
8 Goals conceded are not for (7)
9 Roberto - - - - - -, David Beckham's team mate at Real Madrid (6)
11 Removes from first team (5)
13 Denis Law also played for Manchester - - - - (4)
14 2000s United goalkeeper known by a single name (7)
15 When a player warms-up limbs appear, apparently (4)
16 - - - - - McIlroy, United 1970s/80s midfielder (5)
17 Eric Cantona decided to hang his boots up in 1997 (6)
21 1960s midfielder Carlo Sartori left United for this Italian side (7)
22 David Beckham won a FA Youth Cup - - - - - 1992 (5)
23 Handy go shows 1980s/90s United defender, Mal (anag) (7)

## Down

2 Captain of the Busby Babes who died at Munich (5, 5)
3 Jumping captains like Keane and Ince (8)
4 Very comfortable win for United (4)
5 Goalmouth space (4)
6 Free-kick blocker or ex-United forward, George (4)
9 Dean - - - - -, the scene of United's shock 1984 FA Cup exit against AFC Bournemouth (5)
10 Goal - - - - - - - - - - -, is a timely goalscoring award (2, 3, 5)
12 Colin - - - - -, United forward 1993–94 (5)
13 United were 1994 - - - - - - - - - Cup runners-up (4-4)
18 Football cup matches (4)
19 Dare reveals Newton Heath full-back, Bert (anag) (4)
20 Inter- - - - - Cup for less successful clubs than United (4)

## Across

**1** Des – – – – –, urbane TV football presenter (5)
**7** Attacker versus goalkeeper situation (3-2-3)
**8** Shin pads protect this bone (5)
**10** Long ago fan saw 1970s United forward (anag) (4, 6)
**12** Losing result 1994 Coca-Cola Final against Aston Villa (5, 3)
**14** Newtonards hides nomadic Irish League team, apparently (4)
**16** European ties can be over two (4)
**17** City where United lost in the 1964–65 Inter-Cities Fair Cup to Ferencvaros (8)
**20** 1960s/70s United half-back or defender (5, 5)
**23** Review former England manager Don, apparently (5)
**24** Given a choice, such as with flags on the half-way line (8)
**25** Posts halts play (anag) (5)

## Down

**1** Most up to date score (6)
**2** Has Ian Ure hidden a continent, apparently (4)
**3** A non-league team will be playing soon, apparently (4)
**4** Tony – – – – –, goalkeeper signed from Manchester City 1996 (5)
**5** Illegally produced match tickets (9)
**6** – – – – – – Viollet, United forward 1952/62 (6)
**9** Reg – – – – –, 1950s United goalkeeper (5)
**11** Random examinations for footballers (4, 5)
**13** Spanish camp where ex-United striker Mark Hughes spent some time (3)
**15** Material for matchday programme (5)
**16** Peter Schmeichel signed for Sporting – – – – – – in 1999 (6)
**18** The nickname of side 1970s United forward Stuart Pearson arrived from (6)
**19** Juan Sebastian – – – – –, 2000s United midfielder (5)
**21** First man or Newton Heath forward, – – – – Carson (4)
**22** Take yours at Old Trafford (4)

## Across

**6** 2000s United defender arrived from Leeds United 2002 (3, 9)

**8** Alter null tat to find ex- United forward, Tom (anag) (7)

**9** – – – – – Maradona same forename as *12 across* (5)

**10** Paul, United midfielder 1989/95 (4)

**12** 2000s, United forward, *9 across* – – – – – – made 23 appearances before scoring (6)

**14** One vineyard hides 1930s United full-back George, apparently (5)

**15** Alter capers for 1990s United defender, Chris (anag) (6)

**16** Paul – – – –, known as the Guvnor, who joined United in 1989 (4)

**19** David – – – – –, former United trainee who gained 62 England caps 1990–96 (5)

**21** No links for ex-United defender, Oscar (anag) (7)

**22** 1980s/90s United forward signed from Southampton (5, 7)

## Down

**1** Gets in touch regarding transfers (8)

**2** Alter wader for ex-United forward, Neil (anag) (5)

**3** Soccer stars for adoring fans (5)

**4** Send Don to find Newton Heath forward (anag) (7)

**5** Ban Neville brothers to find girls name (4)

**6** United half-back played in 1958 FA Cup Final (6, 4)

**7** Enjoin dhow for 1940s/50s United forward (anag) (4, 6)

**11** The Red Devils do not hide him, apparently (3)

**12** Well enough to play match (3)

**13** Assistant referee (8)

**14** Goal surround (7)

**17** The game – – – – – down the longer it goes on (5)

**18** 1990s, United defender Paul Parker suffered persistant – – – – – trouble (5)

**20** Not a home game (4)

## Across

**3** 1990s/2000s, United midfielder (5, 4)

**8** After 90 minutes it's finished at Blackburn Rovers FC, apparently (4)

**9** Thrashed the opposition (8)

**10** Position on pitch for kick-off (6)

**13** Alex Ferguson once showed interest in signing striker, Paolo Di – – – – – (5)

**14** Second team player (7)

**15** – – – Brown, 1990s/2000s United defender (3)

**16** Scottish side Alex Ferguson has played for (7)

**17** Nicolas Anelka conceals ex-United forward George, apparently (5)

**21** Avoid relegation (6)

**22** Forename of 1990s/2000s United forward, Mr Greening (8)

**23** Goalmouth space, maybe! (4)

**24** Month in which 1990s/2000s United goalkeeper Roy Carroll was born (9)

## Down

**1** 1970s/80s, United forward signed from Celtic (3, 6)

**2** Rio – – – – – – – – –, 2000s United & England defender (9)

**4** In 1995 Paul Ince left United for – – – – – Milan (5)

**5** Now elks shows United defender, Frank (anag) (7)

**6** Illegal football bribe (slang) (4)

**7** Tire of Old Trafford ground level (anag) (4)

**11** Seats for televised United fans, perhaps! (9)

**12** Wire laden for 1930s United & Scotland forward (anag) (4, 5)

**14** Result or reserve (short) (3)

**15** Midfielder Mickey Thomas signed for United from this Welsh club 1978 (7)

**18** Enclosure feature, maybe! (5)

**19** Steve Bruce broke his whilst playing on his United debut (4)

**20** Alex Ferguson started his managerial career at – – – – Stirlingshire (4)

## Across

**1** Capital city of former United goalie, Peter Schmeichel's native country (10)

**8** Alan Brazil arrived from Tottenham – – – – – – – in 1984 (7)

**9** Peter Schmeichel was one of the best-ever at narrowing this when a forward ran at goal (5)

**10** Offside snare (4)

**11** 45 minutes (4)

**12** High hill hides in ex-United midfielder Carlo Sartori, apparently (3)

**14** Liam, or Billy, Busby Babe who died in the Munich air disaster (6)

**15** It's rude for a player to – – – – – – back to the ref (6)

**18** United's first ever – – – was John Fitzpatrick, 1965 (short) (3)

**20** Rules of the game (4)

**21** Ex-United defender Horace used the whistle! (4)

**23** Alter vanes for 1920s United forward, Sidney (anag) (5)

**24** Lakeside Swiss second division club between Zurich and Bern (7)

**25** United boss 1978–81 (4, 6)

## Down

**1** After Old Trafford, George Best played at Craven – – – – – – – with Fulham (7)

**2** 1920s, United forward Albert is in the paper, apparently (4)

**3** United 1990s/2000s striker Ole Gunnar Solskjaer's international side (6)

**4** Not home supporters at Old Trafford (4, 4)

**5** United beat QPR – – – – –one in the 1968/69 season (5)

**6** Clean wins when United do not concede goals (11)

**7** Wren, holy & rye make 1920s/30s United forward (anag) (5, 6)

**13** Ex-United striker Peter Beardsley started his career at this club (8)

**16** Warn old 1970s United defender, Colin (anag) (7)

**17** Number of years Bryan Robson was United captain (6)

**19** Brag about this Sporting Portuguese league side, apparently (5)

**22** Nationality of 1980s United midfielder, Gordon Strachan (short) (4)

## Across

**1** Put over corner kick, perhaps! (5)
**4** Colour for 1940s United goalkeeper, Robert (5)
**10** United's Russell Beardsmore could have been at Crystal Palace when he received the Young - - - - - of the Month in 1988 (5)
**11** North African country which staged 2004 African Nations Cup (7)
**12** George Best was voted - - - - - - - - Footballer of the Year in 1968 (8)
**13** Alter rage when stepping up the pace at Old Trafford (anag) (4)
**15** Van Nistelrooy & Cantona have been United penalty- - - - - - (6)
**17** Ball motion for rubber cheque (6)
**19** Cool United supporters (4)
**20** - - - - - - - - Zidane, World Player of the Year 2003 (8)
**23** Dennis - - - - - - -, 1950/60s United striker (7)
**24** Frank - - - - -, 1920s United full-back not Mr Ormerod though! (5)
**25** Pads protects these parts (5)
**26** Nationality of 1990s/2000s United midfielder, Roy Keane (5)

## Down

**2** - - - - - Byrne, 1950s United captain (5)
**3** Players who support the main defenders (8)
**5** Long unbeaten periods, perhaps (4)
**6** Type of cowboy film for ex-United forward Enoch West, perhaps! (7)
**7** United's most recent Second Division championship was won in nineteen - - - - - - - - - - (7, 4)
**8** Bandages for parts of the knee (anag) (5)
**9** Newton Heath full-back, whose older brother was a team-mate and Scottish international (5, 6)
**14** Ex-United striker Mark Hughes was born in this month (8)
**16** Ink & loch reveal Newton Heath forward, Joe (anag) (7)
**18** Division One position United finished in 1954-55 season (5)
**21** A side like United has thoughts (anag) (5)
**22** - - - - Gowling, 1960/70s United forward (4)

# The Solutions

## No. 1

```
  R A C E C O U R S E
S   E   H   A   N   W   F
I T A L I A N   D I E G O
R   D   P   C   E   A   R
C O I N   K E R R   R O W
H   N   T   R   D       A
A N G E R S   P O R T E R
R   A   P   G   I       D
L A D   N E I L   D E L L
T   U   M   E   M   R   I
O N T H E   C H A N N O N
N   C   R   E   N   E   E
  S H R E W S B U R Y
```

## No. 2

```
  S H O C K   C L A S H
F   U   H   S   I   A   J
L I L L E   A U S T R I A
O   M   S   V   T   T   M
O N E T H R E E   H O M E
D       I   D   C   R   S
L O S E R S   B O R I N G
I   T   E   H   V       A
G R E Y   N O V E M B E R
H   P   M   U   N   R   V
T U N N E L S   T W I C E
S   E   R   E   R   A   Y
  T Y K E S   B Y R N E
```

## No. 3

```
B A L D W I N   B   Y
  S   O   D   B A Y E R
S T A N L E Y   R   A
O   N   A   L I E R S E
I N T E R   A       H
V   L   L   T   S H I P
I   L A U R E N T   N
P L A Y   N   R   R   G
L       G   F A C U P
R A T T L E   M   C   A
  U   E   R I C H A R D
  G R E E N   N   A   D
  F   K   F I T N E S S
```

## No. 4

```
B L O W N   F   K   P   S
U     E   J O H N E A R P
C L U B S   U   O   L   E
H     B I L L M C G L E N
A   E   X       K   I   C
N I N E T E E N   I S L E
    C   H   R   U   T
B E L L   S A U N D E R S
A   O   D       I   R   T
I N S P E C T I O N     R
L   U   V   A   N O B L E
E A R N I N G S   T     E
Y   E   L   S   D E B U T
```

## No. 5

```
    O  W     F     E     O
 M  I  C  H  A  E  L  C  L  E  G  G
 A     O     V     A     E     R     L
 R  A  N  G  E  R  S     C  R  E  W  E
 K     N     S     K     T           F
 H  E  E  L     I     D  E  F  E  A  T
 U     L     S  A  V  E  D     U     F
 G  O  L  D  E  N     W     T  R  I  O
 H     N     S     D     O     O
 E  V  E  N  T     T  H  E  S  P  O  T
 S     V     O     A     N  E     E
    R  I  O  F  E  R  D  I  N  A  N  D
       L     F     S     S     N
```

## No. 6

```
 P     L     C  U  P  S  H  O  C  K  S
 R  Y  A  N     N     P     N     E
 O     N     F  L  E  T  C  H  E  R
 M  A  C  A  R  I     N     E     P
 O     A     T     C     T     S
 T  E  S  T  S     D  E  F  L  E  C  T
 I     T     T  A  R     D     A
 O  V  E  R  A  R  M     F  A  C  U  P
 N     R     O     G     O     L
    C     T     U     R  O  N  N  I  E
 C  L  A  R  E  N  C  E     N     T
    A     I     C     A     S  O  L  O
 O  P  P  O  N  E  N  T  S     R     N
```

## No. 7

```
    S  H  E  R  I  N  G  H  A  M
 S     T     V     N     O     N     W
 O  P  E  N  E  R  S     A  N  G  L  E
 U     W     N     I     L     E     S
 T  E  A  M     I  D  O  L     R  A  T
 H     R     E     E     I        G
 A  R  T  H  U  R     O  N  E  O  N  E
 M     R     S     E     U     R
 P  U  B     O  N  C  E     S  T  A  M
 T     R     P     O     U     S     A
 O  K  A  N  E     R  U  S  S  I  A  N
 N     G     A     E     E     D     Y
    B  A  I  N  B  R  I  D  G  E
```

## No. 8

```
    P  O  R  T  O     S  T  E  V  E
 A     F     R     E     O     I     O
 S  O  F  I  A     S  E  N  D  O  F  F
 H     E     N     S     Y     L     F
 T  H  R  A  S  H  E  D     A  L  E  S
 O     F     X     C     E     I
 N  U  M  B  E  R     F  O  O  T  E  D
 U     C     R     S     V     E
 N  I  N  E     D  E  F  E  N  D  E  R
 D     U     C     A     N     R     U
 E  L  L  I  O  T  T     T  R  A  I  L
 R     T     L     S     R     W     E
    L  Y  N  E  R     L  Y  O  N  S
```

## No. 9

```
I R E L A N D   H   B
  A   I   O   M I L A N
B L U N D E R   L   T
  P   E   L   O L D H A M
C H E S T   V       T
  M   M   O   E   H I T S
  I   A U S T R I A   E
A L A N   C   S   M   N
  N       A   B I R D S
K E E P E R   P   L   A
    N   R   F O R T U N E
  E D D I E   S   O   C
    S   K   C H A N C E S
```

## No. 10

```
D U T C H   I   S   D   R
A   O   S A N T I A G O
V I L L A   I   E   V   B
I   A L A N D A V I E S
E   M   L       M   D   O
S O C I E D A D   O W E N
  L   N   C   K   E
S T E P   D E C E M B E R
N   N   A       V   B   O
A L A N B R A Z I L     G
T   H   B   R   N O B L E
C L A R E N C E   S     R
H   N   Y   H   S T O P S
```

## No. 11

```
  F   M   M   S   C
S T E V E C O P P E L L
T   R   D   O   I   U   A
E N G L A N D   D E B U T
V   U   L   Y   E     T
E A S T   M   T R E B L E
B   O   R A C E S   O   N
R A N G E R   D   R U U D
U   F   I   S   N   A
C R E W E   R A M S D E N
E   V   R   A   I   A   C
  S E V E N T Y T H R E E
    R   E   E   H   Y
```

## No. 12

```
C   F   V A L E N T I N E
R E I D   R   J   I   E
O   N   E L E V E N T H
S L A V I A   C   D   S
S   L   S   T   T   S
W H I T E   D E F L E C T
O   S   H I D   D   A
R E T R A I N   B A C U P
D   S   G   S   O   L
  M   H   G   P R I N C E
P E N A L I S E   N   T
  S   R   N   N   S O L O
W H I T E S I D E   R   N
```

## No. 13

```
. C O L C H E S T E R .
P A U E . E D . G
A F R I C A N . L E G I A
U R K D E A R
L Y O N . E R I C . R A Y
S L M Y T N
C O L L A R . R E T I R E
H N D D C V
O F F A N O N S E M I
L I G U S L L
E R N I E . B R A M A L L
S A R L H N E
. A L F S T E W A R D .
```

## No. 14

```
. C L Y D E . B L A C K .
T O E D A A J
O L S E N A U S T R I A
M E I V T R C
C H R I S T I E Y O R K
H L D R L B
O L D H A M F U L L E R
R I W I N E
L I S T T R A N M E R E
T S T I E D D
O N E T W O S R A D I O
N N I H U I N
. S T A N D U P P E R .
```

## No. 15

```
R A D F O R D . S . R
. L O A J A M E S
G E O R G I E L A
X W N R E P L A Y
I D E A S A D
A R B N A J A X
W D R O U G H T M
A S K S O E H C
O Z C L E A N
O N S I D E B E R
H O F I T T E S T
D A N N Y L I O
Y S P L A C I N G
```

## No. 16

```
H O M E S T I L D
A Y T R A N M E R E
L I N E S A T S N
V S T E P H E N S O N
E M A R E I
S H A M R O C K B A R S
N S I S L
A J A X C A M P B E L L
S G I U Y O
S P E C T A T O R S F
I R A O S A I N T
S C O T L A N D V U
T F Y Y L E W I S
```

## No. 17

```
. S . R . W . C . B .
A R T H U R A L L M A N
G . A . L . L . A . N A
G A R T E R S . R I G H T
R . R . S . H . K . . T
E R I C . T . S I R C B E
G . N . S E V E N . H . N
A N G L I A . T . H E A D
T . . X . K . H . S . A
E V E N T . E V E R T O N
S . V . E . I . A . E . C
. S E V E N T Y T H R E E
. N . N . H . H . S .
```

## No. 18

```
L . P . M C F A R L A N E
E V E N . H . F . A . O
E . N . . E A R L I E S T
S T A T E S . I . R . E
H . L . T . C . N . S
A S T O N . W A L L A C E
R . I . R O N . R . L
P R E S T O N . B A D G E
E . S . N . K . I . C
. H . L . A . A L B E R T
L E V E L L E R . L . I
. L . A . D . E . A L A N
O P E N G O A L S . O . G
```

## No. 19

```
. L E F T F O O T E D .
G . I . R . I . P . V . S
R A N G E R S . E J E C T
I . E . D . H . N . N . O
M I K E . B E R G . S I R
S . E . D . R . O . . E
B A R B E R . R A M S A Y
Y . . F . S . L . W . M
T R Y . F W E S . Z E R O
O . O . N . X . M . E . O
W O R L D . T R A I N E R
N . K . E . O . N . E . E
. H E A D I N J U R Y .
```

## No. 20

```
. O S C A R . B R O W N .
O . A . M . S . O . E . L
L E G I A . T R O U B L E
D . A . T . A . F . S . A
T H R E E O N E . S T A G
R . . U . D . F . E . U
A L B E R T . F I E R C E
F . R . S . D . F . . T
F O U L . V I C T O R I A
O . N . P . V . Y . O . B
R I T C H I E . T R A I L
D . O . I . S . W . D . E
. U N C L E . W O R S T .
```

## No. 21

```
B A L L A C K . B . P . .
. L . O . H . B A B E S .
A B A N D O N . T . A . .
. E . G . P . S H A R P E
G R A B S . U . . R . . .
. T . A Q P . A C E S . .
P . L A U R E N T . S . .
F A L L . E . R . K . I .
. P . . U . . W I N D S .
L E A G U E . S . N . E .
. L . S . S E A S O N S .
. C A R E Y . M . O . T .
. N . S . F I T N E S S .
```

## No. 22

```
S P U R S . R . M . F . B
E . O . T E N A S I D E .
C L I M B . D . K . N . D
O . . A L F S T E W A R D
N . E . U . . S . L . O .
D O N N E L L Y . V I E W
. C . S . E . S . S . . .
R U L E . C O M P E T E S
I . O . R . . I . S . A .
M I S C O N D U C T . W .
M . U . B . I . E A R L Y
E A R R I N G S . M . E .
R . E . N . S . F E V E R
```

## No. 23

```
. A U . T . P . H . . . .
S E V E N T Y S E V E N .
O . E . T . L . A . R . J
U K R A I N E . R A D I O
T . A . E . R . S . . H .
H I G H . T . R O B S O N
K . E . W I G A N . A . F
O L D H A M . Y . I N C E
R . L . I . D . T . E . .
E L L I S . S W E D I S H
A . A . A . L . V . A . A
. W I L L I E M O R G A N
. D . L . S . N . O . . .
```

## No. 24

```
R . S . P R O M O T I N G
Y O U R . A . A . O . I .
A . P . . P A T D U N N E
N A P O L I . T . R . E .
G . O . D . H . . P . B .
I B R O X . R E F E R E E
G . T . N E W . . O . A .
G R E A V E S . H O M E R
S . R . V . O . . O . D .
. H . T . I . S T A T E S
R E P U B L I C . . I . L
. R . R . L . A . C O L E
J O H N T E R R Y . N . Y
```

## No. 25

| | | W | E | S | T | A | L | B | I | O | N | |
|---|---|---|---|---|---|---|---|---|---|---|---|---|
| C | | A | | H | | R | | E | | O | | H |
| H | O | R | N | E | T | S | | L | A | Z | I | O |
| R | | T | | A | | E | | L | | E | | R |
| I | T | I | S | | O | N | C | E | | S | O | S |
| S | | M | | C | | E | | V | | | | E |
| C | H | E | R | R | Y | | T | U | R | N | E | R |
| A | | | O | | O | | E | | O | | | A |
| S | U | B | | W | I | N | G | | E | R | I | C |
| P | | O | | T | | S | | M | | W | | I |
| E | N | O | C | H | | I | T | A | L | I | A | N |
| R | | T | | E | | D | | N | | C | | G |
| | T | H | I | R | T | E | E | N | T | H | | |

## No. 26

| | C | H | A | M | P | | B | O | B | B | Y | |
|---|---|---|---|---|---|---|---|---|---|---|---|---|
| B | | E | | A | | M | | P | | R | | N |
| I | N | N | E | R | | A | V | E | R | A | G | E |
| L | | R | | S | | N | | N | | M | | W |
| L | E | I | G | H | T | O | N | | E | A | S | T |
| F | | | A | | R | | T | | L | | | O |
| O | N | E | I | L | L | | P | H | E | L | A | N |
| U | | U | | L | | H | | R | | | | H |
| L | I | S | T | | L | E | S | O | L | I | V | E |
| K | | E | | T | | A | | S | | D | | A |
| E | L | B | O | W | E | D | | T | W | I | S | T |
| S | | I | | I | | S | | L | | O | | H |
| | Y | O | U | N | G | | V | E | S | T | S | |

## No. 27

| O | L | Y | M | P | I | C | | B | | P | | |
|---|---|---|---|---|---|---|---|---|---|---|---|---|
| | I | | E | | D | | D | E | L | A | Y | |
| C | A | R | R | O | L | L | | S | | R | | |
| | M | | E | | E | | S | T | A | C | E | Y |
| J | O | R | D | I | | Q | | | | A | | |
| | B | | I | | P | U | | R | U | S | S | |
| R | | T | E | R | R | A | C | E | | T | | |
| H | I | G | H | | I | D | | F | | A | | |
| E | | | Z | | | K | E | A | N | E | | |
| O | N | E | O | N | E | | S | | R | | G | |
| | I | | E | | A | P | P | E | A | L | S | |
| | B | R | Y | A | N | | U | | E | | I | |
| | E | | T | | C | R | Y | S | T | A | L | |

## No. 28

| A | D | D | E | D | | B | | C | | F | | A |
|---|---|---|---|---|---|---|---|---|---|---|---|---|
| F | | A | | L | O | C | H | H | E | A | D | |
| R | O | O | S | T | | O | | E | | Y | | I |
| I | | | T | H | O | M | A | S | R | E | I | D |
| C | | O | | R | | | | T | | N | | A |
| A | P | P | L | E | T | O | N | | Y | O | B | S |
| | | P | | W | | N | | S | | O | | |
| R | O | O | M | | W | E | S | T | B | R | O | M |
| E | | N | | P | | | | A | | D | | E |
| P | R | E | S | I | D | E | N | T | S | | | E |
| L | | N | | T | | V | | E | A | R | T | H |
| A | T | T | A | C | K | E | R | | F | | | A |
| Y | | S | | H | | N | | B | E | H | A | N |

## No. 29

```
    R   B   M   A   F
S T E V E C O P P E L L
U   G   A   O   P   A   G
B L A T T E R   E A G L E
S   L   S   E   A       O
T A L L   O   S L A T E R
I   E   E L L I S   E   G
T E N O N E   X   F R E E
U   G   A   P   R   B
T R I A L   P R I V A T E
E   R   A   R   T   C   S
  J O H N F I T C H E T T
    N   D   L   H   S
```

## No. 30

```
W   H   B R I A N K I D D
H E A D   A   R   I   I
I   N   I N D I R E C T
T E N D O N   W   K   K
E   A   S   I   B   F
S A F E R   M C S H A N E
I   O   A E K   R   R
D E R G O U W   F A C E D
E   D   S   S   E   I
  D   S   T   H A N L O N
V I C T O R I A   O   A
  V   O   I   R   A N O N
D I S P L A Y E D   A   D
```

## No. 31

```
  S I R M A T T C B E
D   H   Y   N   R   O   C
I R E L A N D   A N G L O
C   L   N   R   N   A   R
K I D D   G E R S   N O N
G   O   F   W   F       E
A R N O L D   M E R C E R
R   O   N   R   H   F
D E S   O M I T   P A U L
N   A   D   L   O   R   A
E Q U A L   N E T T I N G
R   D   I   I   T   T   S
  N I S T E L R O O Y
```

## No. 32

```
  S H O P S   C L I F F
L   E   U   I   E   E   P
E A R N S   N I G E R I A
E   O   H   T   S   R   U
L O N D O N E R   H I L L
A   V   R   I   E   T
W H I T E S   A N D R E I
R   C   R   O   T       E
E V E S   O F F E N D E R
N   L   P   F   R   A   N
C H A R L I E   V A N C E
E   N   U   R   A   C   Y
  A D A M S   B L U E S
```

## No. 33

| W | A | L | S | A | L | L |   | T |   | B |   |
|   | C |   | T |   | A | B | R | E | A | K |   |
| M | C | G | R | A | T | H |   | I |   | R |   |
|   | R |   | A |   | E | J | O | H | N | N | Y |
| P | I | E | C | E |   | O |   |   | E |   |   |
|   | N |   | H |   | E |   | N | I | A | I | N |
|   | G |   | A | N | D | R | E | W | S |   | L |
| S | T | A | N |   | D |   | S |   | T | M |   |
|   | O |   |   | I |   | M | A | T | C | H |   |
| I | N | J | U | R | E |   | F |   | N | B |   |
|   | U |   | I |   | A | R | A | B | I | A | N |
|   | P | A | Y | N | E |   | E |   | U |   | I |
|   | N |   | G |   | N | E | V | L | A | N | D |

## No. 34

| C | L | U | B | S |   | C |   | T |   | P |   | D |
| E |   |   | A |   | H | O | M | E | G | A | M | E |
| L | I | B | R | A |   | P |   | A |   | L |   | N |
| T |   |   | I | N | T | E | R | M | I | L | A | N |
| I |   | N |   | G |   |   | S |   | I |   | I |   |
| C | L | E | M | E | N | T | S |   | U | S | E | S |
|   | W |   | R |   | W |   | G |   | T |   |   |   |
| W | E | S | T |   | F | O | U | R | T | E | E | N |
| O |   | P |   | T |   |   | I |   | R |   | E |   |
| L | E | A | G | U | E | G | A | M | E |   | W |   |
| V |   | P |   | R |   | I |   | E | X | A | C | T |
| E | V | E | N | I | N | G | S |   | I |   |   | O |
| S |   | R |   | N |   | G |   | S | T | E | I | N |

## No. 35

|   |   | B |   | M |   | B |   | F |   | W |   |
| H | A | R | R | Y | C | L | E | A | V | E | R |
| O |   | O |   | E |   | A |   | I |   | B | H |
| R | E | T | I | R | E | D |   | L | I | B | R | A |
| A |   | H |   | S |   | E |   | U |   |   | R |
| C | H | E | W |   | L |   | T | R | E | V | O | R |
| E |   | R |   | R | E | V | I | E |   | A | Y |
| B | O | S | S | E | S |   | M |   | F | L | A | G |
| L |   |   | V |   | D |   | V |   | E |   | R |
| E | R | N | I | E |   | E | T | I | E | N | N | E |
| W |   | E |   | A |   | N |   | L |   | C | G |
|   | B | I | L | L | F | I | E | L | D | I | N | G |
|   | L |   | S |   | S |   | A |   | A |   |   |

## No. 36

| C |   | R |   | A | T | T | A | C | K | E | R | S |
| R | O | A | D |   | E |   | L |   | I |   | O |   |
| O |   | D |   | R | O | C | H | D | A | L | E |   |
| S | O | C | C | E | R |   | O |   | D |   | E |   |
| S |   | L |   | Y |   | H |   |   | E |   | W |   |
| B | R | I | A | N |   | J | O | E | D | A | L | E |
| A |   | F |   | S | O | L |   | R |   | T |   |
| R | E | F | E | R | E | E |   | W | E | L | S | H |
| S |   | E |   | L |   | C |   | Y |   | E |   |
|   | U |   | I |   | E |   | R | A | N | G | E | R |
| L | E | E | R | O | C | H | E |   | O |   | E |   |
|   | F |   | A |   | T |   | W |   | P | A | U | L |
| B | A | N | N | I | S | T | E | R |   | L |   | L |

118

## No. 37

|   | A | G | G | R | E | G | A | T | E | S |   |
|---|---|---|---|---|---|---|---|---|---|---|---|
| B | F |   | A |   | L |   | N |   | V |   | J |
| R | E | F | E | R | E | E |   | D | I | E | G O |
| Y |   | A |   | Y |   | V |   | E |   | N | H |
| A | V | I | V |   | K | E | R R |   | S | O | N |
| N |   | R |   | F |   | N |   | S |   |   | N |
| R | E | S | U | L | T |   | N | O | R | W | A Y |
| O |   |   | E |   | L |   | N |   | H |   | B |
| B | O | B |   | T | R | I P |   | M | I | K | E |
| S |   | R |   | C |   | T |   | H |   | S | R |
| O | M | A | G | H |   | T | R | A | N | T E R |
| N |   | C |   | E |   | L |   | L |   | L | Y |
|   | G | E | O | R | G | E |   | V | O | S | E |

## No. 38

|   | S | T | U | D | S |   | M | A | T | C | H |   |
|---|---|---|---|---|---|---|---|---|---|---|---|---|
| W |   | I |   | O |   | W |   | L |   | O |   | S |
| A | N | T | I | C |   | A | G | A | I | N | S T |
| T |   | L |   | H |   | S |   | N |   | T |   | R |
| E | L | E | V | E | N | T H |   | D | A | L | E |
| R |   |   | R |   | E |   | D |   | C |   | T |
| L | I | G | H | T | S |   | C | E | L | T | I C |
| O |   | O |   | Y |   | H |   | C |   |   | H |
| G | O | U | W |   | R | E | L | E | G | A | T E |
| G |   | R |   | S |   | A |   | M |   | I | R |
| E | L | L | I | O | T | T |   | B | U | R | K E |
| D |   | A |   | L |   | H |   | E |   | E | D |
|   | L | Y | D | O | N |   | G | R | A | S | S |

## No. 39

| S | W | E | D | I | S | H |   | D |   | F |   |   |
|---|---|---|---|---|---|---|---|---|---|---|---|---|
|   | H |   | E |   | T |   | P | E | T | E | R |
| L | I | N | E | K | E | R |   | V |   | A |   |
|   | T |   | P |   | P |   | C | A | I | R | N S |
| F | E | E | D | S |   | A |   |   |   | O |   |
|   | H |   | A |   | D |   | R |   | I | N | T O |
|   | O |   | L | A | U | R | E | N | T |   | T |
| J | U | N | E |   | N |   | Y |   | A |   | I |
|   | S |   |   | N |   | B | L | A | N | C |   |
| P | E | D | D | I | E |   | R |   | I | G |   |
|   | R |   | M |   | D | O | N | A | G | H Y |
| C | A | M | P | S |   | W |   | N |   | A |   |
|   | W | S |   | L | E | E | S | I | M | S |   |

## No. 40

| R | O | V | E | R |   | P |   | L |   | R |   | M |
|---|---|---|---|---|---|---|---|---|---|---|---|---|
| U |   | X |   | A | N | D | Y | C | O | L | E |   |
| S | P | A | I | N |   | F |   | O |   | B | L |   |
| S |   |   | T | O | M | C | O | N | N | E | L L |
| I |   | D |   | B |   |   | S |   | R |   | O |   |
| A | L | A | N | B | A | L L |   | S | T | A | R |
|   | V |   | Y |   | E |   | G |   | S |   |   |
| A | V | I | D |   | F | O | U | R | F | O | U R |
| S |   | D |   | B |   | E |   | N |   | A |   |
| S | C | H | M | E | I | C | H | E | L |   | M |
| I |   | E |   | N |   | L |   | N | O | T E S |
| S | T | R | A | C | H | A | N |   | G |   | E |
| T |   | D |   | H |   | P |   | B | O | B B Y |

119

## No. 41

```
. N . S . I . J . S .
P R E S T O N N O R T H
A . A . E . T . H . A . S
T E R R A C E . N I G H T
C . M . M . R . S . . R
R A I L . S . R E N N I E
E . S . D E V O N . O . T
R U S S I A . N . E R I C
A . . S . C . S . T . H
N I M E S . R I T C H I E
D . A . E . A . U . E . R
. F R A N C I S B U R N S
. K . T . G . S . N
```

## No. 42

```
R . H . O L E G U N N A R
Y E A R . I . A . E . L
A . M . . B E R N A B E U
N U M B E R . D . R . X
G . E . A . N . U . S
I B R O X . R E F E R E E
G . I . P E R . U . C
G U N N E R S . A G G R O
S . G . E . P . U . N
. F . Y . M . E D W A R D
F I N A L I S T . Y . L
. F . R . E . E . D A V E
W A N D E R E R S . N . G
```

## No. 43

```
. H A R R Y M O G E R .
D . E . O . E . N . D . L
W O R R A L L . E A G L E
I . B . D . L . T . A . A
G R E G . P O S H . R E G
H . R . W . W . R . . U
T I T L E S . R E S I D E
Y . . A . M . E . R . G
O L D . L I A M . U E F A
R . I . A . R . F . L . M
K E V I N . I M I T A T E
E . E . D . N . V . N . S
. P R E S T O N E N D
```

## No. 44

```
. J A P A N . R E A C H .
N X V . T . M . A . H
O L I V E . R O M A N I A
B . N . R . I . A . T . R
B I G M A T C H . S O L O
Y . . G . K . Y . N . L
S O C C E R . D O N A L D
T . O . S . B . U . . B
I S L E . T R A N S F E R
L . O . N . A . G . R . A
E N G L A N D . B L A S T
S . N . M . Y . O . M . T
. L E V E L . T Y K E S
```

## No. 45

| C | R | O | S | S | E | S |   | A |   | W |
|   | O |   | K |   | A |   | B | R | Y | A | N |
| A | G | A | I | N | S | T |   | E |   | L |
|   | E |   | P |   | Y |   | C | A | R | L | O | S |
| D | R | O | P | S |   | O |   |   |   | F |
|   | B |   | E |   | M |   | U |   | C | I | T | Y |
|   | Y |   | R | I | C | A | R | D | O |   | H |
| A | R | M | S |   | K |   | T |   | C |   | E |
|   | N |   |   | E |   |   | S | A | M | M | Y |
| R | E | T | I | R | E |   | T |   | C |   | O |
|   |   | I |   | E |   | B | O | L | O | G | N | A |
| M | E | D | A | L |   |   | T |   | L |   | T |
|   |   | S |   | D |   | D | O | N | A | G | H | Y |

## No. 46

| L | Y | N | A | M |   | A |   | C |   | F |   | D |
| A |   |   | S |   | O | N | E | O | N | O | N | E |
| T | I | B | I | A |   | O |   | T |   | R |   | N |
| E |   |   | A | L | A | N | F | O | G | G | O | N |
| S |   | D |   | L |   |   | N |   | E |   | I |
| T | H | R | E | E | O | N | E |   | A | R | D | S |
|   |   | U |   | N |   | O |   | P |   | I |
| L | E | G | S |   | B | U | D | A | P | E | S | T |
| I |   | T |   | V |   |   | P |   | S |   | I |
| S | T | E | V | E | J | A | M | E | S |   | G |
| B |   | S |   | R |   | D |   | R | E | V | I | E |
| O | P | T | I | O | N | A | L |   | A |   | R |
| N |   | S |   | N |   | M |   | S | T | O | P | S |

## No. 47

|   |   | C |   | D |   | I |   | S |   | A |
| R | I | O | F | E | R | D | I | N | A | N | D |
| O |   | N |   | W |   | O |   | E |   | N |   | J |
| N | U | T | T | A | L | L |   | D | I | E | G | O |
| N |   | A |   | R |   | S |   | D |   |   | H |
| I | N | C | E |   | H |   | F | O | R | L | A | N |
| E |   | T |   | N | E | V | I | N |   | I |   | D |
| C | A | S | P | E | R |   | T |   | U | N | D | O |
| O |   |   | T |   | S |   | A |   | E |   | W |
| P | L | A | T | T |   | L | I | N | K | S | O | N |
| E |   | W |   | I |   | O |   | K |   | M |   | I |
|   | D | A | N | N | Y | W | A | L | L | A | C | E |
|   |   | Y |   | G |   | S |   | E |   | N |

## No. 48

| L |   | F |   | N | I | C | K | Y | B | U | T | T |
| O | V | E | R |   | N |   | N |   | U |   | I |
| U |   | R |   | T | R | O | U | N | C | E | D |
| M | I | D | D | L | E |   | W |   | G |   | R |
| A |   | I |   | R |   | L |   | A |   | N |
| C | A | N | I | O |   | R | E | S | E | R | V | E |
| A |   | A |   | W | E | S |   | M |   | I |
| R | A | N | G | E | R | S |   | N | I | C | O | L |
| I |   | D |   | E |   | F |   | H |   | D |
|   | N |   | E |   | X |   | E | S | C | A | P | E |
| J | O | N | A | T | H | A | N |   | I |   | W |
|   | S |   | S |   | A |   | C |   | A | R | E | A |
| S | E | P | T | E | M | B | E | R |   | S |   | R |

## No. 49

|   | C | O | P | E | N | H | A | G | E | N |   |
|---|---|---|---|---|---|---|---|---|---|---|---|
| W |   | O |   | A |   | O |   | W |   | I |   | H |
| H | O | T | S | P | U | R |   | A | N | G | L | E |
| I |   | T |   | E |   | W |   | Y |   | H |   | N |
| T | R | A | P |   | H | A | L | F |   | T | O | R |
| E |   | G |   | C |   | Y |   | A |   |   |   | Y |
| W | H | E | L | A | N |   | A | N | S | W | E | R |
| A |   |   | R |   | T |   | S |   | A |   | O |
| S | U | B |   | L | A | W | S |   | B | L | E | W |
| H |   | R |   | I |   | E |   | S |   | D |   | L |
| E | V | A | N | S |   | L | U | C | E | R | N | E |
| S |   | G |   | L |   | V |   | O |   | O |   | Y |
|   | D | A | V | E | S | E | X | T | O | N |   |   |

## No. 50

|   | C | R | O | S | S |   | B | R | O | W | N |   |
|---|---|---|---|---|---|---|---|---|---|---|---|---|
| S |   | O |   | W |   | S |   | U |   | E |   | H |
| E | A | G | L | E |   | T | U | N | I | S | I | A |
| V |   | E |   | E |   | R |   | S |   | T |   | R |
| E | U | R | O | P | E | A | N |   | G | E | A | R |
| N |   |   | E |   | P |   | N |   | R |   | Y |
| T | A | K | E | R | S |   | B | O | U | N | C | E |
| Y |   | I |   | S |   | F |   | V |   |   |   | R |
| F | A | N | S |   | Z | I | N | E | D | I | N | E |
| I |   | L |   | A |   | F |   | M |   | D |   | N |
| V | I | O | L | L | E | T |   | B | R | E | T | T |
| E |   | C |   | A |   | H |   | E |   | A |   | Z |
|   | S | H | I | N | S |   | I | R | I | S | H |   |

122